For all stroke survivors and loved-ones around the world.

'Anger, denial and great rehabilitation are key motivators to stroke recovery in the early days. Early acceptance of a bleak prognosis – both by the survivor and health professionals – is more likely to leave an individual the way they are. Don't lower your expectations, raise them. Think positively and look forward to the day you will Laugh Out Loud again!'

Kate Allatt 2012

All brain injured patients, who can think normally, must not think IF function will come back – but WHEN. Then they must actively seek to restore movement back.

Kate Allatt March 2012

Life is limitless ... you just have to believe in it!

Kate Allatt 2011

Contents

Prologue

I was relaxing on a sun lounger, immersed in both good and bad memories, enjoying the heat of the sun. Suddenly, a strange, male, English south London voice interrupted my daydreaming.

'Hello, what are your names?'

I looked up to see a middle-aged man directing the question at my three best friends and me.

'Kate, Jaqui, Alison and Anita', we responded politely, though none of us were really that interested in any sustained conversation so we kept our answers brief. Having said that, we discovered he was a solicitor from Essex. A very chatty one who could talk the hind leg off a Spanish donkey, I'm sure.

This confident stranger is quickly nicknamed Mr. Guest, because he has the uncanny physical similarities to Liza Minnelli's ex-husband! It was quickly apparent that Mr. Guest is up for a laugh, although generally, at his own expense! He insisted we chatted to him to keep him amused, as his friends didn't seem overly interested in his child-like repartee.

The banter and wine started to flow, as did Mr. Guest's witty tales, for the rest of the afternoon by the pool.

At 6pm we said our goodbyes and retired for an early evening meal and round of cocktails, whilst they departed to Magaluf to enjoy some end-of-season dancing.

The next morning, at around 8.15am, Alison and I woke up after a refreshing night's sleep and visited a local pub for an al fresco milky coffee and chat in the early morning sunshine. We were minding our own business when guess who arrived?

Yes, looking extremely frazzled, worse for wear and cradling an array of plastic water bottles, it was none other than our special holiday friend.

Mr. Guest had spent the late evening (and most of the twilight hours) dancing with his party of other middle-aged mates, along with Magaluf's late-season revellers. That morning, it was fair to say, Mr. Guest had definitely misplaced his sparkle!

After sharing a bottle the previous afternoon, Alison and I decided to hatch one of our typically wicked plans. (Especially with the svelte like body he didn't have!) Thankfully, he was up for a laugh. His inner Superman bravado came to the fore, and he agreed to meet Jaqui and Anita in the hotel lobby at 8am the next day.

However, Alison and I decided to hatch one of our typically wicked plans. You see, during the previous early evening pool banter with Mr Guest, Jaqui and Anita had suggested giving him an early morning run around Palma the next day. The only problem was that he, 'didn't do running!' (A svelte running body he didn't have!)

But after sharing a bottle or two of wine with us, his inner Superman bravado came to the fore. He finally relented, and agreed to meet Jaqui and Anita in the hotel lobby at 8am the next day.

However, one big problem! The normally habitual and reliable runners, Jaqui and Anita, had remarkably overslept until 8.30am that morning, as we had departed to local pub and breakfast coffee shop. They were only able to dress themselves to run just before 9am that morning.

This gave me an idea! I hatched a plan with Mr Guest and Alison in pub which was to play a trick on my old running pals, which he found a far too much of a mischievous challenge to refuse.

In the short period of time that we had got to know him the previous night, he seemed very trusting and, better still, up for a laugh.

Rising to the challenge, Mr. Guest agreed to return to his hotel room to model his own brand of fetching leisure wear, complete with trainers. Furthermore, he added his own touch of authenticity with his faked sweaty wet patches under his arms and on his chest. At 10am, that same morning, he agreed to stride into the hotel breakfast room to appear like a vision in Lycra in front of Jaq and Anita.

It all went to plan. Jaq and Anita tucked into their breakfast buffet, having enjoyed their unusually late morning run in the sunshine. Next, right on cue and executed perfectly, Mr Guest arrived at our breakfast table huffing, puffing but – more importantly – sweating!

His voice sounded slightly irritated.

'Where were you at 8am? I waited until 8.15am then had to run alone, I hate running!'

Jaq and Anita sheepishly fell for the wind up, as I collapse into a fit of 'stroke' laughing. For the record though, Jaq was quick to spot the all too familiar 'Kate and Alison wind up', but we did all laugh all the way back to the sun loungers!

The holiday fun was just beginning.

Us buddies were most definitely back on top form.

To our special holiday 'Guest', whoever you are, you're a real trouper.

Thanks for the holiday laughs!

'Life is limitless... self belief and hard work is all you need!'

Kate Allatt 2011

12

Chapter 1 –
Double Take

For new readers to my story who may not have read my first, shoot-from-the-hip book, 'Running Free: Breaking Free From Locked-in Syndrome', here is a helpful potted recap!

I'll take you back to 9am on Sunday 7th February 2010.

'We are going to the walk-in medical centre now. I'm fed up of your bloody moans about your headache. Get your handbag!' (I now know that my husband Mark was secretly as worried as I was but tried to hide it from our kids and me.)

'Ok', I thought, as India, Harvey and Woody (then aged 11, 10 and six), were bundled into the car.

Mark had been uncharacteristically masterful whereas I, unusually, happily accepted being told what to do.

The weekend nursing sister noted my symptoms with calm, professional concern, so as not to worry India or me. I had been slurring during the check-in reception procedure. However, as I described my dizziness and pins and needles (with my 'classic stroke symptom of angry headache), she sent me immediately to Accident and Emergency at Sheffield's Northern General Hospital – a full 20-minute drive away.

Mark hadn't observed my slurring speech. He'd been struggling to park the car, with the excitable boys in the back.

We arrived at A&E by midday. I waited and waited to be seen whilst cradling my head in a useless attempt to stem my intense, piercing headache. When the junior doctor finally did his assessments, he seemed overly preoccupied with my lifestyle and the fact that Mark had not witnessed my slurring.

My blood pressure was in the 'normal range,' although that level was actually very high for someone with normally very low blood pressure. My brain was never MRI scanned.

The doctor concluded it was likely I was suffering from a stress-induced migraine headache. Interestingly, I'd never suffered with migraines in my life. Nor had I previously visited a hospital, other than to give birth three times. He deduced that the migraine was probably caused by my high-stress lifestyle. I had been juggling establishing a new business, rearing three young kids (pretty much single-handedly as Mark travelled overseas), helping with homework and after-school activities, cooking, cleaning and shopping. So it was really plausible, right? We all returned home somewhat relieved that all I needed was some Co-codamol, sleep and some T.L.C. I slept from 2.30pm until I awoke at 5.34pm with my head feeling as if it was gripped tightly in a vice. The boys were arguing loudly (again) in the bath. I got up to sternly reprimand them. Lowering myself gingerly on my sofa downstairs, I again cradled my painful head. Mark was in the kitchen making my favourite cup of Earl Grey tea. Suddenly, I experienced a continuous strange, loud, bizarre buzzing sound in my head. I panicked, shouting out:

'Mark, what's happening to me?'

6.09 pm on 7th February 2010. This time is permanently etched inside Mark's memory.

Mark heard my loud gobbledygook as my words spat out jumbled. He instinctively knew something was desperately wrong and darted into the lounge where he saw me slide off the sofa into a heap on the floor. I was unable to respond to his scared, desperate cries.

Quick-thinking India spotted our neighbour Lise – fortunately, a nurse – outside our house at that precise moment and summoned her indoors. Lise gently put me in the recovery position as Mark, now extremely worried, dialled 999. Shortly later, two ambulances arrived at our Dore home where a paramedic found me drifting in and out of consciousness. I felt completely out of it and felt a warm sensation from down below. I knew I had wet myself in my non-matching underwear! The next thing I heard was the loud voice of the rather concerned paramedic who was urgently administering oxygen to me.

'Kate, are you there? Talk to me.'

I heard, but I couldn't respond.
I also heard Mark's worried voice.
'Is it an epileptic fit?'
'No', replied the paramedic.
'I'm afraid it's more serious than that.'

My world seemed to end. It felt reminiscent of the scene in the Terminator Film, as Arnie is slowly lowered into the vat of molten steel. Blackness.

Looking back, I still can't believe how lucky I was that Mark was at home that day. He could have so easily been at work when I was alone in the house. Or I could have been out solo running over the windswept and wintry Peak District fells with not another human in sight to give me the urgent help I needed. I try not to dwell on it.

If I had died there and then, I wouldn't have known it, as my last breaths were involuntarily exhaled out of my body. This morbid memory now gives me some relief from the worry I have always had about dying. I now know my kids saw me stretchered out grey and lifeless, and assumed that their invincible mummy was dead. I don't remember the half hour ambulance journey to the Northern General, but I do remember the intermittent, conscious, painful leg cramps on the hospital trolley and being incapable of relieving any of my excruciating pain.

My mum recalls how I physically fought from my ICU bed as I was being put into a medically induced coma. I don't remember that. There was nothing. No Hollywood style ethereal dreams in soft focus, no escapist thoughts, no hearing my relatives whispering softly into my ears pleading for me to wake me up. No nothing.

I wasn't aware of my brain scans taking place, nor can I fully interpret them now!

My life missed three days.

This medically induced coma was a typical treatment for an acute brain injury such as mine. It was later diagnosed as a Basilar Artery Thrombolitus. The actual medical diagnosis was: *A right vertebral artery dissection and occlusion on 7/2/10 with an acute infarction of the pons.*

I was high on the opium based, pain killers, which gave me some very vivid and extremely lifelike 'trippy'

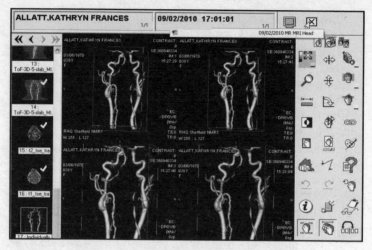

My brain two days AFTER my stroke, clearly showing no evidence of recannalisation or blood flow. The broken line on the right of the image shows a series of dashes. My total blockage and a third partial blockage of the right Pons of my brain. © Kate Allatt

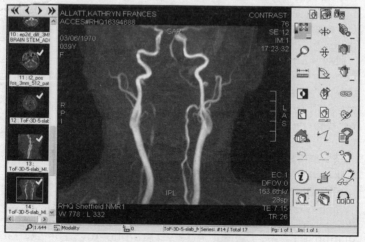

The faded area (or Thrombolitus) on the left of this image (though the right pons side) shows my injury. There is a total blockage where the blood didn't pump through my brain. © Kate Allatt

hallucinations which left me scared senseless. Thank God I've never done drugs! I specifically recall one. I was in a Guernsey Café, bizarrely still in my hospital bed, talking to a character from the book I had recently been reading prior to my stroke entitled: *'The Guernsey Literary and Potato Peel Pie Society'*. A wartime story set on the Channel Islands. I might as well have been stranded alone on an island, as my new reality was so far removed from my life before. I was stuck on my own battlefield in a war

THE GRAPHITE DRIP VERSION ②

The particularly vivid and distressing nightmare.
© Kate Allatt

I did not know how to win. My lively mind was battling to make my inert body rise up and fight: not play dead when I needed it most. I wanted to scream – but of course that was impossible. My 39-year-old body, which I had always kept in tip-top health wouldn't let me. I felt cheated.

The large oral obstruction more commonly known as my life support machine would have prevented any noise leaving my paralysed lips anyway. However much I tried to shout, no sounds of letters were formed by my paralysed tongue or even whistled out of my still lips.

THE CRAMPS
VERSION ①

'Suffering in silence.' This depicts my painful leg cramps and the 4 hour stopwatch illustrates the frequency with which I was turned by nurses. © *Kate Allatt*

I wanted to pat my head, kick my legs, flick my arms, and change my uncomfortable position. Nothing. I couldn't relieve my dreadful cramp either.

It does make me think that patients like me should be moved more frequently than once every two to four hours. It was every four hours in the rehabilitation ward, later reduced to every six hours in order to prepare me for what would happen for my life in a nursing home.

The only good thing, stuck in my total hell, was that my debilitating headache had at last gone. RESULT!

The hubbub of the High Dependency Unit, (part of ICU) with the mainly business-like, emotionless nurses – along with the tubes and noises from the machines positioned on both sides of my bed – made me feel SHIT SCARED!

It may be A Daily Mirror type tabloid headline but I really was, 'Trapped In My Own Body Unable To Move Anything But Feeling ALL the Pain!' The most horrendous kind of torture you can imagine.

If I had been buried alive, then this is what it would feel like. In my less than glamorous state, I had tubes coming

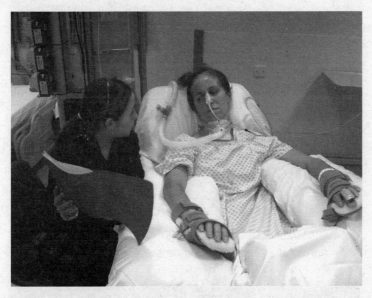

Grown-up 'mummy' India visits me in ICU and shows me her homework. Normality right? Week 2 © Kate Allatt

out of every orifice. From my mouth (to breathe for me), my nose (to feed me), my nether regions (to urinate) and my arms (for drugs and fluid). Previously, my life had been hard at times, but this took toughness, pain, insecurity and fear to a thousand new levels. Complete hell. (Which makes childbirth seem a walk in the park)!

In between my 'rabbit-caught-in-the-headlights' bouts of total fear and utter helplessness, I had a steady stream of anxious thoughts about my children swirling around inside my head.

'Who is picking the kids up from school?'
'Are they doing their homework?'
'Are the still doing their after school activities?'
'Why haven't I seen them yet?'
'Why can't I just die and have done with it.'

I went to hell and back, then hell again, every minute of every sodding day, as all I could do, assuming that my head was positioned correctly, was gaze at the simple white, analogue clock on the wall which felt like my full

19

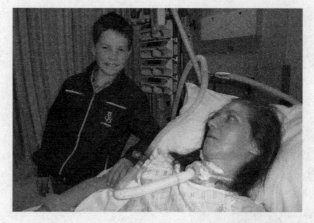

Harvey wanted to see me but his forced smile hides his utter fear of doing so. © *Kate Allatt*

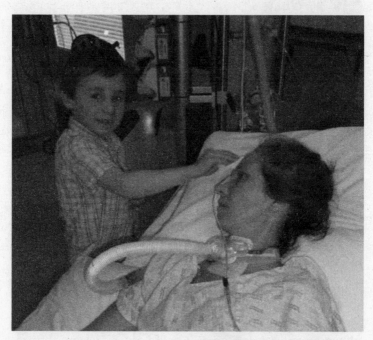

6 year old Woody braves a smile too for me. Week 3 ICU
© *Kate Allatt*

time roommate as I waited for the few authorised visitors I'd actually permitted to see me in that state.

During the later weeks in intensive care, I had to learn how to forget all about my life as a mum. I focused on remembering my pre-maternal life as a teenager. My separation anxiety was so painful at that time that I had to pretend they never existed at all, just to cope. Heartbreaking. But true. So SORRY for you to read this kids!

There were some lovely caring nurses in ICU, but there were also a lot of nurses who seemed robotic. I was just a patient, not a real person with feelings. I know they must have cared but at the time I felt they were just going through the motions. ICU is a place I never want to return to – even though that sounds so ungrateful – because it still gives me nightmares now. When I wrote my first book, I struggled to open up these buried emotions back then. Even now unlocking those thoughts, feelings, experiences and terror now, is still incredibly painful.

I will try to emphasise a few things about that time then, because it may just help family and friends whose loved ones are suffering a similar fate to mine.

Sure, I had a personal TV with retractable arm, attached to my bed, but the nurses were too busy keeping me alive, to remember (or even prioritise) switching it on.

With Mark, I'd spend an hour blinking my preferences to the TV guide, which was often a waste of our time. I used one blink for no and two blinks for yes.

I was so consumed by my solitary, dark thoughts, my wide-awake nightmares and my multiple weeks of insomnia. I worried about my plight, my health, my life and impending painful death and my kids. Every single minute of the day.

The mental torture was intense, as were my desperate, trapped thoughts.

'What has happened to me?'

'How long will I be like this?'

'My mouth is so dry, I need a drink.'

Why isn't Mark here, by my side, ALL the time or am I not that important to him?'

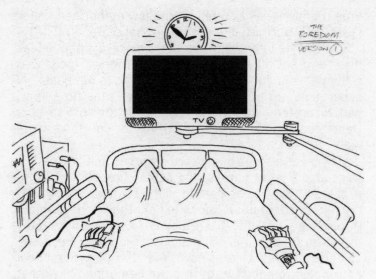

Basic human right – T.V. or docking station which were actually switched on & off by nurses. © Kate Allatt

'If this is the physical extent of my crippled and pathetic life, couldn't Mark just slip a pillow over my mouth and nose and just be done with it?'

It's true to say that I wanted my husband to end my life, right there and then, but he never gave me the opportunity to spell this out or even ask me that question. Bizarrely, Mark told me, only two weeks before my stroke, these strangely prophetic words. Words I could now distinctly remember in horror and apply to myself.

'If I couldn't wipe my own arse, I would want to die.'

My well-known 'Graphite drip' dream in ICU (Running Free) was so 'real.' I had been paranoid I was going to be allowed to die. I even complained months later to nurses in Osborne 4 and my mum, via my letter board. But back in ICU, I SO wanted to die.

I wanted to end my intense physical pain, the scary tracheotomy 'pop offs', the sustained insomnia, the emotional torment of being trapped inside my own body, the utter indignity, the lack of communication for weeks, the hallucinations and the emotional separation anxiety

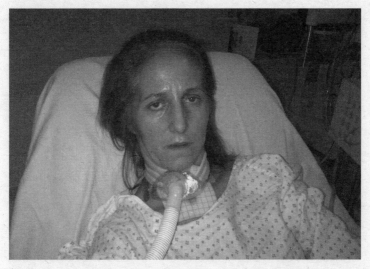

'Look into my eyes.. then take that bloody camera away now!'

from my kids. Which is why I intermittently blocked them out from my mind as a coping mechanism. It pains me to even read this sentence but it is important to state it was how I felt THEN. I was administering the 'cruel to be kind' behaviour to MYSELF to save me from further torment at not being with them.

Sure, I didn't want some strange nurse collaborating in my death, instead of my beloved Mark. Around those dark days, I concocted the idea that maybe my loved ones had already made that awful decision. Would they turn off my life support if I took a turn for the worse?

My head was positioned correctly towards the door when I spotted my eldest, my daughter India, and proceeded to cry uncontrollably. (Mark had asked doctors if it was OK for her to visit me just three weeks on and I'd been fitted with a tracheotomy and stomach feed, or PEG, by then.)

India was shocked, upset and distraught by my tears and distressed at the huge number of tubes. She enveloped me like a mum would embrace her daughter. At that point, our roles became reversed.

23

My firstborn child adopted a nurturing mothering role as I crumbled tearfully, like a newborn baby. India chatted with such confidence and poise. She shared news about her schoolwork, friends, etc. Not that dissimilar to our cosy chats in the kitchen at home. She duly stayed forty-five minutes before hand signalling to her Dad, 'T', for 'Timeout'. She left my bedside and proceeded to vomit everywhere with the shock of seeing me in that state. Grandma Ann, from Southport, was on hand behind the scenes to comfort in the ICU waiting room but I was unaware of that. India's visit had moved and inspired me and I will never forget her courage.

I mentioned the physical pain, in the form of leg cramps, from wearing the vital leg splints to minimise my 'foot drop' and to also prevent shortening of my finger tendons. The leg and arm splints were very hot, causing severe pain, burning and cramps. I used the trusty analogue clock on the wall to ensure they were promptly removed on time.

My insomnia was totally frightening. My fears, my pain of not being turned enough, my new strange world, and all of my anxieties were heightened and intensified during the dark, cold, winter nights. The nurses would huddle around an empty bay for nighttime chats and coffee. This would be a 'tease too far for me,' as I was mostly a 'nil by mouth' patient in hospital. I was in total despair.

All I had to do in the night time in my dimmed ward of four beds was listen to the hissing of my life support breathing for me, the bleeps from my sats oxygen machine and that bloody clock on the wall. (Now my roommate from hell!) Seconds were like minutes; hours were like days, weeks like months. I dreaded the severe loneliness and stillness of the night hours.

There was light at the end of my dark tunnel when my friend Jaqui, broke the rules and unofficially broke my communication silence. Together with Alison and Anita, she sneaked in a cobbled-together, homemade letter board and was damn well on a mission to test their theory that I could in fact understand. They were proving a point to medics, but mainly wanted to give me a chance to try and communicate in some way. I wanted to battle back so much and unbeknown to me they had arrived with a secret strategy.

My best friends were prepared to take the risk pissing off the medical staff, on my behalf and I for one welcomed their rebelliousness. They wanted to find a way to understand what I wanted and to help me be more comfortable.

Jaqui spoke with clarity and authority.

'Kate, we know you can understand, but we need to know what more we can do to help you.'

Until that point, my silent yet wet emotional tears of self-pity, pain and loneliness had demonstrated clearly to my loved ones that I was fully compos mentis or fully cognitive.

'I need you to blink once for no and twice for yes.'

She then asked me to test her theory with a yes/no question.

Jaq pointed to each scribbled letter, whilst she said the letter sound out loud.

She said, 'A' I blinked once. 'B'. Blink. 'C'. Blink. 'D'. Blink. We continued all the way to the letter 'S'. Blink blink. The happiness on my friends' faces was palpable – their rows of smiles like a loop of celebration bunting and I heard them say those breakthrough words.

'Kate's blinked twice!'

I knew I had limited physical energy, so I had to spell out the key word of that sentence and only hope that they would correctly second-guess what I was trying to communicate.

Excitedly, all 'the girls' repeated and remembered the letter 'S'. Ok, next letter. 'A'. Blink 'B'. Blink. 'C'. Blink. 'D.'Blink. This routine continued all the way to two blinks on 'L' when Jaq then put me out of my misery rightly guessing the word, 'SLEEP' and to confirm she was right I blinked twice! I was jubilant. I welcomed my friends' rebelliousness. The cavalry had arrived.

It felt like there was a bottle of Cava popping inside me!

'Thank f*** for that!'

Write 'End of Word' on the communication board so your carer knows you haven't forgotten how to spell! © Kate Allatt

In her own excited frenzy, Jaq excitedly went onto to guess, 'what...want to sleep?'

'Can't sleep?'

I blinked twice, YES.

'OK, so you can't sleep... at night?'

I blinked twice. They understood. Inside my sleep-deprived head, I screamed with delight.

'Alle'f-ing luia!'

The girls immediately left my bedside and demanded some sleeping pills for me off the ICU nurses. Finally, for the first time in weeks, I slept like a baby all through the night.

During my subsequent visit from Mark, it's fair to say that he struggled with this board, as did my mum. (I also faced difficulty when trying to communicate with my new Locked-in friend Michelle Wheatley. More about her later.)

For example, if your visitor looks at the letter board as opposed to the patients' eyes at the point of blinking, it is easy to miss the number of blinks given which is really frustrating for everyone. Furthermore, it's important to keep track of the letters that have been spelt out, because if the visitor forgets the letters in the word, we had to start the word all over, which is exhausting – especially for the patient.

Some visitors, really thought they are trying to help me by second-guessing the letter I wanted to spell out. It wasn't helpful and actually bloody annoying and deeply, deeply frustrating. They were often wrong and when I indicated as such, they would wildly second guess any other random letter before giving up on the word I was trying to spell-out in the first place.

I think it's also worth noting that the basic, non-colour coded letter board that I used later in ICU, had no box on the letter board stating that it was the 'End Of A Word' which was also infuriating. The absence of that box meant that Mark thought my brainstem stroke had left me with an inability to spell!

In her typical style of wild exaggeration, my mum gave me one particular piece of advice, which turned out to be brilliant hope for my recovery. She said in a matter-of fact way.

'All you need is to make new pathways, as they don't ever disappear, so you just have to make new ones.'

Little did I know back then, but this piece of advice in ICU gave me the small glimmer of hope that I would later draw on in Osborne 4 to fight and 'will' myself better. I now know that her statement was a slightly stretched version of the truth as she deliberately missed the word 'voluntary' before 'pathways'.

But it was a pivotal moment for me.

These words fired me up and I imagined my limbs moving again. I was now Rocky Balboa setting out to prove my doubters wrong. Suddenly, I knew I had to change my mindset and somehow force myself to believe that I would break free from this hellish existence. I would 'go the distance' and come out of this. But little did I know just how challenging my physical fight would be – not to mention the mental anguish of unexpected challenges. I had to trust in the nurses as well as myself...but sometimes this proved difficult. When you are Locked-in, you feel so powerless when medical equipment fails.

Oxygen whizzing into the air & not my lungs, was an unnecessarily scary regular occurrence. © Kate Allatt

The tracheotomy pop-offs were totally chilling, and a frequent occurrence, which sent fear, panic and complete insecurity throughout my body. During those pop-offs, I was often lying five yards away from my one-to-one ICU nurse. Trust me, a long distance when I couldn't breathe any oxygen for myself with a 'Don't Let Me Die!' expression I hoped the nurse would understand. Generally, it was only matter of a few seconds until my ICU nurse replaced my tube but it felt like an eternity.

With oxygen gushing into the atmosphere and not into me, I lay helpless and was unable to alert anyone as to what had happened.

This was by far the scariest thing to ever happen to me.

My daily bed and bath routine, with often two or three other nurses was totally abhorrent to me. I clenched my eyes closed tightly, in the hope that everyone would just disappear. As one nurse administered my four hourly drugs cocktail, another would sponge me down. Another would massage my rather expensive Clarins cream onto my arms and legs. Another nurse would change my

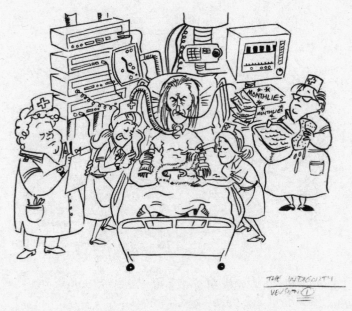

Nappies at 39 years of age! Talk about regressing!
© Kate Allatt

'nappy' or 'Inco' pad or incontinence pad. At around seven weeks, she uttered the horrifying words:

'Look who's started her monthlies? We'll have to get some pads off your mum, won't we?'

'Just great!' I thought.

I can't breathe for myself; shit alone; enjoy a proper soak in a bath or shower; wee; eat; drink; walk or even move a muscle, except my eyelids. Now, just when I thought things couldn't get worse, my bloody periods have returned with a vengeance. No time for roller-blading then! (think annoying 'san ads') I wasn't able to drink, then I was, and then I wasn't, as they discovered I was drowning in Earl Grey tea, as it caused me to silently aspirate into my lungs. The fluid was soaking into my lungs instead of my gullet.

I have since often thought how most of life revolves around the ability to taste, eat and drink. Can you imagine life without it? A stomach or 'PEG' tube with no Christmas

Charades in I.C.U. with Alison. Will she eventually understand my eye gaze? © Kate Allatt

dinner, birthday cake, chips, or steak would administer all your daily sustenance. No coffee with friends in a café, or a celebratory glass of Cava. No Earl Grey tea, my favourite cuppa.

I never looked in a mirror to see the new me but I knew that my hair must have needed dyeing (after seven weeks) and that my eyebrows were probably as unkempt as my legs, which I could see through the bottom of my eye if I glanced downwards.

However, to cap it all off, I had an unwelcome hospital visitor in the form of my usual heavy period that someone else had to deal with. The last thing I was willing to return. Still, I suppose my body had regained some 'normal' function in that respect.

During my early hospital hell are two abiding funny memories of the 'charades' with Alison as she leapt around my hospital bay as she tried to figure out what I was looking at. Was it the sink? My banned Earl Grey teabags? My moisturiser? My blanket? Each time she would ask, 'Am I hot?' where I would blink once, and she eliminated options. After many minutes of this game she figured out that my gaze was in fact towards the fire escape door because I wanted to outside in my special blue, bed/chair in the middle of winter!

The other memory is of Mark having to sit outside in the snowy hospital garden wearing just his work clothes, no coat, while I was snuggled up in numerous warm blankets.

On those long, cold, darkest days, I would strongly recommend the TV is a necessity for patients as they need mental stimulation and being left continuously with your own thoughts can be depressing.

I would also suggest that each ICU or stroke unit has a 'nominated patient advocate.' That individual would kick into action for patients with similar symptoms to mine, as early as week one or two. Their role would be to quickly ascertain if the patient could:

a) Understand most things.
b) Find ways for them to try and communicate in any way.

Furthermore, that specialist person should be psychologically trained to try and explore and prepare the patient's feelings and emotions – and also prepare the patient for the huge challenges ahead.

My right thumb flickered half a millimetre during week eight. I met this defining moment in my recovery with outstanding indifference at the time.

'That's a good sign,' said my ICU physiotherapist as I clung to his comments with all my life.

Now, you will be amazed to learn that at the time of writing it is late summer 2011. I know I am incredibly fortunate to be out of my 'Locked-in' state, out of hospital and out of the country – on a much-needed holiday with Jacqui, Anita and Alison. I am free! One year on since my hospital discharge, just two things are on my mind. Working on my suntan, and working on how others can benefit from my stroke story.

Here are my five most important recommendations:

1)   Tell a patient (if they can comprehend) that
      they will never lose voluntary neural pathways,

should they hopefully return. It took me eight weeks, but others anything from three days. Muscles WILL fatigue in the early days, (from the under-use), but there is everything to play for and offer sleeping pills early on.

2) WORK BLOODY HARD!!! A Sister in ICU, who had previously worked in Osborne 4 said:'Kate, you just go there and work bloody hard in rehab.' I took her words SO literally.

3) Give every patient a nominated patient advocate, early on in ICU.

4) Turn the TV on (even banal programmes). It's vital and NOT a luxury.

5) Please add the box 'end of word' on the letter board in ICU, if it's not already on there.

During a visit from Anita one Friday afternoon, we got the long awaited news.

The ICU nurse announced to us late that I would be moving out of ICU that night! I was so excited inside, in fact, we both were. She immediately texted Mark.

It was late and I worried it wouldn't happen, with every passing minute there was no sign of a transfer ambulance, so we were both anxious. To great relief, it was to be much later that night, when I was moved – a milestone on the road to recovery.

8.10pm Friday I was transferred to Osborne 4, Rehabilitation Unit, Northern General Sheffield.

I don't really want to dwell on my experience in Osborne 4, because I've already written stuff that I felt at the time of writing of my first book. There are however, a few fundamental things that I feel compelled to express which will hopefully help others. In addition, there are a few indulgent anecdotes that were previously unpublished in my first book that I want to share.

I arrived in Osborne 4 on a trolley full of excitement – quickly quashed as soon I realised that I was gaining a less personal one-to-one, 24-hour nursing care and the toughness of a disciplined rehabilitation regime.

Was I ready for that shock? No way. It was horrific, scary and lonely. Believe it or not, I actually wanted to return to the safety and security of ICU! It's a bit like looking forward to seeing a light at the end of a tunnel only to realise the lights belong to an oncoming train!

With morning routines of bed bath or horizontal shower, drugs, dressing and moisturising, it was a military regime designed to rehabilitate me in some small way. The fact it took two nurses to shower me (and four to hoist me out of my bed and onto a shower table) meant my feelings of indignity went stratospheric!

Every day, I was 'timetabled' with one hour of physiotherapy, one hour of occupational therapy and one hour of speech therapy. Book and music group was thrown in for extra measure.

Ever wondered how you could play a keyboard with no hands and no bodily movement, apart from my side-to-side head movement?

The answer? An adapted laser and helmet probe with a remote keyboard. (Now, you don't get that on X Factor!) I contemplated my changed routine.

'How had my life really come to this?'

There were many stories in Osborne 4 and some very fond memories. Most nurses really got to know me, Kate the patient, over the six months I was there and I received pretty special treatment from them.

For example, one late spring day in April 2010, Mark's folks, Ann and Kev, came for a visit, ready to give me a bit of fresh air in the hospital grounds. Our forced upbeat chat was always one-way with my visitors, hence why most people visited me in two's! But that particular day left me particularly hysterical. Being a traditional Yorkshire bloke, Kev delighted in driving me in my manual wheelchair, with 'posh' headrest, out of the hospital front door, which was usually locked with an intercom access.

We had gained approval from Sarah, the nurse, but that's where the confusion occurred. With the green light to go outside from Sarah, Kev took me off on a mission, out of the building and over 800 metres away!

He pushed me out of the building and up the pavement to a sunny, grassed area. We sat in the sun for one hour. Suddenly the tranquillity of the day was broken when we heard the screams of female voices in the distance. As they became louder we heard the voices shouting.

'KATE! KATE! KATE!'

Kev and Ann leapt up and signalled our position in a friendly 'do come and join us' way.

It was only Sarah and Jackie; it only turned out that there was a miscommunication about 'where' outside I was going. Sarah meant immediately adjacent to my ward, Kev thought he understood otherwise! Sarah and Jackie's panic was because a patient was absent without leave at the Northern General Hospital, WITHOUT the necessary emergency trachea breathing equipment bag, should my breathing deteriorate suddenly. Kev got his knuckles wrapped well and truly, but it won't surprise you that I laughed my socks off metaphorically and inside my head!

Shortly after this time I had a change of focus. In Alison's words, 'I got my spark back!'

I willed and willed my body every hour of every day to prompt the speed level of my recovery rate. I imagined my new pathways getting longer and longer, until after many weeks I could make them flicker myself. My sheer bloody mindedness, guts, obsession with my early intensive, committed therapy got me here. FACT.

I wasn't a miracle and I wasn't divine intervention. It was bloody hard work, great therapy, support, my fitness and unshakeable self-belief.

People often asked me since leaving Osborne 4,

'What was the most emotional moment of my recovery?'

That's easy and probably hugely surprising.

It was when my big, left toe flickered ½ millimetre, for the first time.

If I could make that big left toe move, with that being the farthest pathway from my brain, then game-on for the rest of my still yet paralysed left side. I made my big left toe move by my relentless 'willing.' I used to lie and stare at my left toe and think 'move damn you!' I used to imagine I was at the funfare playing the 'Test of Strength' game. In

Moving mountains 'willing my left side to move and it actually doing so, was a monumental moment in my miraculous recovery'. © Kate Allatt

my mind I was holding a heavy hammer which I thumped on the peg, sending the puck skywards metaphorically to ring the bell at the top. One day, I would be out of this bloody wheelchair (which I totally detested, even though I needed it) and I began to believe that I would not only walk again, but would run again too.

When I tried a simple button activated with my thumb to work the Grid 2 communication computer, it opened up my world again. (Though I only ever thought it was a temporary measure until my voice returned. I later discovered it was always considered a permanent feature by my pessimistic speech therapist team!)

So fast forward months of relentless work.

I remember when I got fitted for my new joystick operated electric wheelchair and abused my newfound,

35

Grid 2 communication system on a short visit home.
© Kate Allatt

independent speed! I drove the wheelchair around the rear grounds and sped off against the explicit instructions of the ward manager, with my rude gesticulation to 'go away'! I could escape and certainly tried to by zooming over the bumpy grass, which I know created a huge potential health and safety issue for him and me.

An innocent bit of fun perhaps, but the ward manager seriously reprimanded Mark for flouting health and safety regulations. Mark was given the first, of two possible verbal warnings on my behalf! Another strike for me and I would be out! Oh, yes please!

The other story relating to the electric wheelchair was a particular time when Mark and the kids visited me. We decided to visit the basketball court attached to the rehabilitation centre. They marked out a basic, but fun, slalom course with cones. First India, then Harvey, Woody and Mark, took separate turns to operate my joystick, whilst running alongside me being weaved around the cones, in a time trial. Then it was my turn! I rammed the joystick in forward pelting down the court, except the ball on top of the joystick came off in my hand and the actual joystick jammed so I continued to propel forward. I ended up crashing into the cone, much to the amusement of us all.

Every day another patient, Ali, would relieve the boredom of being on Osborne 4 with me, as we participated in our daily electric wheelchair races on the ward. We used to nod to each other our intent to do it from the nurses station, though I'm might add that his was a faster model and he always won!

Finally, I will say that I was protected from my own prognosis at all times. My friends and family did an amazing job. I will always be immensely grateful. I really, truly believe that the mind and self-belief is more capable and powerful than we will ever give it credit for, hence my mantra.

'Life is limitless.' Kate Allatt February 2011.

'It's not the circumstance, it's your reaction to it, that counts.' Dr AL SIEBERT – author of 'The Survivor Personality'.

Instinctively, 'willing' and repetition is what I did right before the first small signs of my recovery. Did I force something my recovery to happen? Definitely. Would a less extensive recovery have happened to me anyway? Possibly. Did I accelerate my recovery? Definitely. I obsess about going to the gym and pushing my rate of progress and peoples' expectations.

Interestingly, author Norman Doidge M.D a psychiatrist and researcher, wrote about neuroplasticity in his book, 'The Brain That Changes Itself: Stories of Personal Triumph from the Frontiers of Brain Science.' It's definitely worth a read.

So what do I think we could learn from my experience?

Every stroke is different. Fact. Some strokes, brainstem or otherwise, are more severe than others.

But I already know plenty of examples of brainstem stroke recoveries – nationally and internationally. I may be unique in the speed and extent of my recovery from the severity of my particular injury, but my brainstem stroke recovery is NOT unique. Because of the slowness with which my body came back to life and months of dependency on a tracheotomy, stomach feed, catheter, communication and mobility equipment, my recovery has astonished medical professionals.

At the Northern General hospital there was also undoubtedly some great nursing and intensive therapy, combined with my total obsession to get 'normal', but here are some other things that may or I hope should resonate with you and other families and friends affected by brainstem stroke with or without Locked-in syndrome.

My particular brain injury was very severe and my treatment was not the norm in cases like mine. I did had a stroke of luck with my care.

Repetition and 'willing' help. Get Norman's book!

· Establish and fully understand the patient's own goals. The therapists, doctors and nurses must always be patient-centred. My psychologist famously said in private to Alison, that, 'Kate must lower her expectations.' Alison rightly said, 'No, you need to raise your game! Raise your expectations to meet Kate's!'

The idea that a patient like me, somehow 'plateaus' in terms of recovery is really just another way to say that rehabilitation funding post NHS hospital discharge runs out. My personal opinion, so keep working!

For any medical professional, I urge you to use my story (and those of others I know) as an antithesis to the doom and gloom you may have given up until now. Furthermore, please enforce some of the positive messages I received too.

Finally, I can't stress the need for early rehabilitation for EVERYONE (with a largely positive outlook). My left side didn't flicker for 3.5 months: I first shuffled in a baby stroller after 5.5 months, I was nil-by-mouth for 6.5 months, and so was I a 'no-hope' case? Would medics have given me treatment elsewhere? Norman gives a clear warning.

'Neuroplasticity has the power to produce more flexible but also more rigid behaviours – a phenomenon I call

'the plastic paradox.' Ironically, some of our most recent stubborn habits and disorders are products of our plasticity. Once a particular plastic change occurs in the brain and becomes well established, it can prevent other changes from occurring...'

IN SUMMARY

WHEN MEDICS QUOTE NEGATIVE STATISTICS TO FAMILY, FRIENDS AND CO-WORKERS, PLEASE BALANCE THIS OFTEN ALL-TOO-EARLY BLEAK PATIENT PROGNOSIS WITH EXAMPLES OF REAL, POSITIVE STORIES OF PEOPLE WHO ARE NOW RECOVERING FROM THEIR BRAINSTEM STROKES (WITH OR WITHOUT Locked-in SYNDROME). DONT LET THEM QUASH ALL HOPE AND PATIENT SPIRIT. LOOK AT ME! HELP THEM FLY!

Chapter 2 –
Girls On Tour

Yippee! Flights and hotel booked. Travel insurance and currency sorted. I'd arranged the childcare and set the 'out of office' email reply from both my Fighting Strokes charity and KateAllatt.com websites.

Three nights in Majorca awaited us. Sunshine here we come!

Us 'girls', Jaqui, Alison and Anita, were full of hopeful anticipation of the holiday fun ahead. Yet we had all resigned ourselves to the fact that the experience on the now infamous and wonderfully named 'Champagne O' Clock' luxury yacht, of two years ago, couldn't possibly be beaten.

When we enjoyed champagne cocktails on board, it was by far the most unbelievable 'blag' we had ever experienced and represented a very brief reminder of a former carefree period of our lives, i.e. pre-stroke, pre-kids, work and family responsibilities. (As described in 'Running Free' last year).

We had shared many fond memories and jokes surrounding that first short break to Majorca, even continuing to chat about the luxury yacht experience at dinner parties. Much to the annoyance of our husbands fed up with hearing it for the umpteenth time! Those mad maritime memories gave me the distraction that I needed from the loneliness and isolation of my lengthy Locked-in hospital nightmare.

However, my best friends and I, two years on, billed this new short break as the 'comeback' tour. After our 18 months of pure unadulterated hell – I never underestimated the effect my stroke had on them and their families too – we all believed that we were all due a bit of fun.

This break was very timely, especially after all my physical and charitable hard work, (though some would say obsession). We had always planned to celebrate my recovery and our remarkable reunion, but I also wanted to use this holiday to thank my friends for their unwavering, sustained support.

This getaway was all about total escapism, rest, relaxation and sun, especially for Jaqui, (a keen sun worshipper). I had a self-imposed ban when it came to my teccy stuff'. No iPhone, iPad or laptop. I was totally incommunicado. Bliss!

I was going to let my hair down and be 'normal' and forget about 'Kate, the brainstem stroke survivor'- the label I had worn for the past year. I was damn well going to unleash the pre-stroke 'up-for-a-laugh' Kate, and was looking forward to being just been one of the 'girlies' again. I make no apology for this term as we are all in our 40s and yet we are 'youthful' in terms of both spirit and adventure.

Would strangers notice that I was more delicate than my counterparts? Yes. Though they didn't need to know anything about my life at all. I was not going to mention it, if at all possible. This holiday was not just about me – it was for our friendship group to nurture and thrive.

Jaq, in her rather fabulous black soft-top Mercedes (not a Thunderbird convertible but still very 'Thelma and Louise!') rolled up at Anita's house a full 10 minutes earlier than she needed to. We had plotted to trick Anita into getting ready for 4am, so she would be unusually on time, for a change. Anita is well known for her inability to be on time for anything. Ever! So this time we took a 'no risks' approach, so she was waiting for Jaq as she pulled up.

Me next, then onto Alison's house, although Jaq saw far more than she bargained, as she peered through the stained glass front door at Alison hurriedly sorting out the last minute touches to her outfit. Giggling, we set off to Manchester Airport with the wind blowing in our hair. It felt invigorating and just like the old times we shared. I was determined to enjoy every minute of this freedom.

Jaqui is extremely efficient and organised. Our luggage allowance had been well planned with heavy shared items packed and stowed in the airplane hold as opposed to my hand luggage. The only problem I had to face was that I had forgotten to seal my eye lotions and potions in clear bags in my hand luggage. Whoops! A small glitch in my otherwise, fastidious preparations.

On the flight over I was anxious about suffering from a Deep Vein Thrombosis and wrestled with my friends for the Thrombo-embolus deterrent (T.E.D.) stockings issued courtesy of the airline. I now knew every risk of stroke there was and could have kept a conversation going for the whole flight – but kept my mouth zipped. I did not want to become a bore, and it felt it was time to chill out and stop worrying.

Jaq and I sat together and soon the banter and giddiness was in full flow. We were all going to have a great time. It is Jaqui who first predicted that we would be sunbathing by the Spanish hotel pool by 12.30pm when in fact it was actually bang on midday, a whole half hour earlier! Our schedule was organised with military precision and our excitement grew every minute and became more heightened as we learnt from the BBC weather report that there was to be hot Mediterranean sunshine, as expected, for the next four days. Bring It On!

As we approached our hotel, I felt we were all getting on as brilliantly as we always have. Not one of my friends made a big fuss about my limitations. I perhaps didn't walk as quickly or as steadily as I used to, but I looked and acted like normal Kate again and they did not treat me with kid gloves. I felt up for most things and had packed some new holiday outfits. Whether or not I could dance like I used to was another matter! We were all buzzing with excitement by the time we had unpacked, and headed to the pool area.

By the pool it was fairly quiet, as it was the end of the season, and I instantly felt that all my responsibilities were a lifetime away. Stretched out on sun loungers, it seemed as if we all gave a collective sigh of relief that we could put my stroke experience momentarily behind us and soak up the sun.

'Phew, do I need this break!' I told myself as I felt all the tensions, worries and dark memories of my hospital 'break' dissipate in the warm breeze. I felt *so* relieved that I was holidaying with my best friends again.

As I stared towards the inviting pool and its still, ripple-free surface, I mused that my life was now calm and safe. I left the others relaxing and walked to the water's edge. I didn't need their help, I told myself. But even though I thought I'd go for a swim, I hadn't properly thought *how* I was actually going to get *into* the pool, as it had no sloping edge access.

I tried to lower myself onto the pool's edge on my knees and slide my legs around into the inviting sparkling water but I had a problem.

'Oh S***'.

As I precariously tried to lower my body. I quickly realised I didn't have the prowess or power in my muscles to lower myself from my standing position into the pool.

After 20 minutes, I noticed growing, unwanted attention from other sun worshippers as they witnessed my unusual poolside version of the Hokey Cokey.

So, forced to abandon my ill-thought efforts, I nonchalantly scuttled back to my sun lounger. Hopefully, people thought I had only planned to dip my toes in the water – not go for a swim.

Yes, I do fail at some things!

Settling down on my sun lounger, I remembered how exactly one year ago to that very day I was discharged from hospital – my 'home' for just under eight months. As I relaxed in the afternoon sun, celebrating this incredible anniversary with my top mates (and of course, the obligatory glass of Cava), I marveled at what I had achieved during last 18 months. Unbeknown to me, my brainstem stroke was billed by the medics as having a very likely different outcome.

For example, if I had a solitary life with 24-hour care, I would no longer be an active participatory mum in my kids' lives. Instead, I would be an observing 'by-sitter' from an adapted wheelchair. This upsets me greatly even to dwell on it.

Imagine no walking, moving, talking, swallowing, eating, kids sports day, shopping trips, Christmas-at-home, and girlie trips abroad would have been a definite no-no. A life I could not have mentally envisaged or accepted back then.

Fortunately, I was initially mentally protected from this. I never knew my early medical, prognosis or my expected future limits. However, I now understand that around only small percentage worldwide ever recover from this Locked-in stroke injury – with most ending up forgotten about in a nursing home.

In such places, you would probably get – at best – sporadic weekly emotional and physical help. How does that maximise your quality of life and enjoyment?

As I sunbathed, I felt the warmth of the sun on my skin and I asked myself some intense questions. Past events had seemed so very surreal. I now have time to think quite deeply about how I broke out from being Locked-in.

'How did I get here?'

I pondered on others' initial expectations for my recovery and felt quite distressed to think I could have believed I was 'trapped' indefinitely.

Yet here I was gazing at a cloudless blue sky, *not* a ticking clock on a nursing home wall. I felt so happy yet I couldn't help but think of others view of my life plan post-stroke. All I know is that I am one of the lucky ones.

Does that junior A&E doctor ever recollect his unforgivable and monumental f*** up with my initial misdiagnosis? In the interests of fairness, I accept that I should have had my persistent headache checked out earlier but I was let down big time when I did.

Perhaps, I underplayed the severity of my symptoms, as most busy mums often do. However, a scan would have revealed that a stroke was extremely likely to occur and steps could have been taken to minimize its effects. When it happened, I would already have been in the safest place in the world, and not half an hour away from medical help – crumpled on my lounge floor.

How much did my self-belief and relentless 'willing' (some would say obsession), and practice contribute to my remarkable recovery?

How did my incredible support and relentless positivity affect my stroke outcome? Furthermore, are fit people more likely to recover from this type of injury? (As I had been a 70-mile a week fell runner and was proud of my running achievements).

Exactly which types of brainstem strokes are recoverable? Is there any published data? Are some families and early, brainstem stroke survivors given their long-term prognosis too soon by medics, after the incident?

Do doctors in general, try too hard to emphasize the patient's poor chances of recovery, which in turn totally quashes any early hope and patient motivation?

In fact, do doctors even really fully understand this condition at all? Are early intensive rehabilitation therapy services in the UK really so woefully lacking?

I have often thought how lucky I was to be living in a Sheffield postcode. A stroke patient's chances of recovery should not be linked to where they live.

When this holiday was over I would try and fix a meeting with Deputy Prime Minister Nick Clegg, my local MP. I had some important questions, which needed answers. (More about this later!)

As explained in chapter one, I had initially felt every single ache, cramp and pain with no way of easing it. I had totally given up on life. To make matters worse was my inability to communicate anything until the ICU nurses introduced a very basic letter board (which took considerable weeks to sort).

Being 'cognitively normal,' but paralysed from the eyelids down, after awaking from my three day coma left me in a dark, desperate, frightened, insecure place. A solitary hell from which I feared I'd never escape.

So, being here in Majorca now is a bit of a bittersweet moment. The pain, the emotional strain and the relentless hard work is set against the jubilation, (against the odds), of me walking out of hospital on crutches on Wednesday 29th September 2010 at 11.05am.

The evidence is there for all to see on my YouTube channel 'runmadkate'.

What a difference a year makes!

As I rubbed on more suntan lotion, I recalled all the times nurses and friends applied moisturizer onto my lifeless limbs. Then, I was helpless and scared and dependent on others. Now, I was abroad with my best friends, away from doctors, nurses, carers, physios and speech therapists. I was more or less my own person.

I had been given a second chance and a new life. One I was going to grab with both hands and never take for granted *ever* again.

For the first time in a very long while, I felt as free as a bird.

Chapter 3 –
Retrospective

You'd think that at the end of September, Majorca would be quiet. Wrong!

It seems that bagging one of the sun loungers by the pool was still a difficult early morning task! I rolled off one hotel bed, walked a few steps, and rolled onto another – my poolside sun lounger. Lounging was definitely what I had in mind. I was SO grateful for my four days off from my relentless personal physical training, the growing interest in my Fighting Strokes charity, the launch of my personal speaking career and of course my little angels! We had hours of time ahead gossiping, relaxing and reminiscing about our shared times together as we sipped chilled drinks and topped up our tans. No longer the delightful shade of 'palest hospital white', I felt healthy and happy. What could be better?

The relatively dull (for me), sun-basting activities, meant that I would often zone in and out of the banter, meanwhile Mr. Guest was pushing for a game of volley ball on the court next to the pool.

During my zoned-out time, I thought how enormously proud I was of my first non-fiction book –'Running Free.' It was totally unique in terms of the speed in which it was written and published after my stroke. I also know people laughed as much as they did cry, when they read it. Sure, I didn't pull any punches, with my candid descriptions, anecdotes and criticisms at the time. But it was a painfully honest account of how I felt back then. It makes me so happy to know that my book is used as a practical tool for other new brainstem stroke patients and importantly their supportive families and friend, who want ideas on what to do for the best. I know it enabled me to leave a legacy for my kids, which gives me great comfort.

My advice also is that if you don't like the advice you are being given by your doctors, try and go elsewhere. Don't just let them extinguish all your hope and fighting spirit.

Was I still angry and in denial when I wrote my first book? Definitely.

Was I sometimes unfair to Mark, my hugely supportive husband, most of the time? Yes.

Did I get the best NHS therapy services the UK has to offer? You bet.

Did my medical team have one eye on the depressing statistics and past patients' progress, rather than being patient-centred with me? Definitely.

My brainstem stroke and subsequent Locked-in Syndrome threw a huge spanner in my otherwise lovely life. It was a vivid, honest, upbeat, undiluted account of MY emotions at that time, both good and bad.

Interestingly, since the racist murder of Stephen Lawrence more than 18 years ago, his mum recently said that her anger kept her going in her campaign to bring his killers to justice. It was anger – though used in a very different way – which kept me going too. We should never underestimate this emotion and how it can be used positively.

Apparently you go through anger and denial during and after a stroke which, albeit on a far different level, shared similarities with his mum's grief and years of utter injustice. Being in that hospital bubble, where nothing seemingly happened fast enough for me, or when the nurses and/or doctors promised me things which never came to fruition made me SO angry inside. But *how* could I let it out. I could not lash out physically or shout – as most people express anger. It imploded internally as I absorbed it inside my tortured mind. My tears fell silently. I was angrier than an erupting volcano yet nobody could see it. At times, I visualised myself standing on top of local beauty spot Win Hill as I shouted my head off. Manic screams ringing around the beauty spot into the valley below. I often pondered if this internal Primal Scream therapy would be unleashed in months to come? How I felt back then was raw and very real but I had no way of letting off steam. To outsiders, I was the passive patient

I told you I'd do stairs! Now start listening to nurse Kate!
© Kate Allatt

and my internal wailing battle cry went unnoticed – which further pissed me off!

I remember being angry with my team of healthcare specialists, whose hand I forced, because they didn't allow me to start learning how to walk up the rehabilitation stairs in hospital. Well, that was until I broke their rules first on a home visit with my step dad, Dave. Fortunately, time has taken the edge off some of my early raging emotions.

Furthermore, the separation anxiety for nearly eight months from my three young, cherished kids aged 11, nine and six, was immense and can never be underestimated either.

However, for the record, I do feel compelled to set the record straight on a few other points.

Firstly, I owe my Yorkshire born husband, Mark, a bit of an explanation, perhaps an apology – even though it's well known that you lash out at those closest to you.

Mark is a 45 years old, reasonably successful, ex-Rugby Union full-back. He is physically in great condition thanks to his love of mountain biking in the Peaks. As the eldest of two siblings, born to Ann and Kevin from Southport; he was the 'blue eyed boy'. We met in my first year at Sheffield City Polytechnic, and shared many drink-fuelled student nights out.

After dating for 10 years, Mark finally made an honest woman of me! In May 1998, we were married in Sheffield at Dore's Christ Church on a beautifully hot day. We went onto share many marital ups and downs, but we have lasted over 21 years together! As parents to our three children, India, Harvey and Woody, we were a 'normal' family, right? (You see the word 'normal' used a lot by me!)

I have responded to my paralysed, physical demeanour in the public glare, as some sort of brainstem stroke crusader. I was proud of my new, post-hospital, 'stroke look' compared to my ICU look, even though I did differ from the old Kate. For me my first book pictures, magazines articles, TV and newspapers stories had portrayed at my worse. I.e. a pale, frail bag of tiny bones, dribbling with grey undyed roots.

But contrast that with my pride at being let out for good behaviour, to attend Woody's sports day, last July 2010? I have been told since, how I shocked the normally reserved 'Dore set' at my first public appearance. For me though, it was summed up in Arnie's famous words, 'I m back!'

Mark is a very kind, proud husband and father, but hugely work driven. (I'd go as far as to say he's a workaholic, like me!) He is very practical, often fixing the computers, lighting, TVs and monitoring the solar panel efficiency.

He was always fairly reserved and has never been overly affectionate. Even his hospital bedside love and cuddle levels were sadly lacking, much to my annoyance. I lay alone for hours, wishing and hoping that Mark would get into my bed (ignoring health and safety protocols), and envelop me with a reassuring, loving hug. We now know he would only ask for help if his life (or mine) depended on it!

My good friend Anita often describes Mark as wilful and I would agree! He is also very private, like his parents. Believe it or not, he remarkably didn't even share any

My man! Afternoon visit at home with Mark May 2010.

news of my stroke with his sales team for four months at work. Perhaps he was escaping or burying his head?

All that said, it is important for me to say: MARK CHANGED THE COURSE OF MY LIFE!

A fact that I failed to stress in my first book. Sorry Mark! (Even I've not forgotten how you comically refused to turn my arm back from palm-up to palm-down, after I learnt my new one-way arm flipping trick during our weekend visit in my wheelchair!).

You see Mark did knowingly (when he was at breaking point) and unknowingly mess up at times, but his 'management of the doctors and nurses' in ICU (along with my ill-coping Mum), ensured that I received the unusually early intensive rehabilitation care at the one of the country's most highly regarded NHS rehabilitation units, Osborne 4. He also stood by me through it all.

THANK YOU MARK, for being bolshy, political, with a small 'p', standing your ground and insisting that I received the early, intensive rehabilitation when I did. I didn't go to The Hallamshire Hospital, with their less intensive rehabilitation (as I understand it to be the case), which generally cares for stroke survivors twice my age.

I often wondered if his successfully engineered outcomes for me were largely the result of his persevering management of the medical teams (because of the initial alarming A&E cock up), as well as my postcode and my young age working in my favour.

On reflection, apart from feeling bloody lucky to still be alive, I know that I received (on balance and in comparison to other sufferers), a superb level of nursing and therapy.

I got to know the nursing staff's personalities and there were those who made key events as fun as possible. The French and Saunders Double Act of Osborne 4 went beyond the call of duty with their upbeat humour and words of encouragement when they first brought me back for an emotional visit home and shopping trip – you helped make the challenging times a real joy. I must also thank brilliant student nurse Kerry who helped get my body moving again and helped me 'bridge' for the very first time as well as those chatty ones who painted my nails and did my hair. The NHS needs more people like this bunch who got the fact I was a woman, not just a patient, and I needed a boost to my self-confidence on my road to recovery.

Big thanks also go to my regular nurses who regaled me with amusing stories of their weekends in the big wide world as they washed me every morning. For example, one such anecdote I fondly remember was a conversation they were having where one nurse innocently thought that my original honeymoon destination (I spelt it out via a letter board) was Tuscany in Africa! Not forgetting the lovely student nurses who carefully plaited my hair and painted my nails, which I duly smudged!

I am thoroughly indebted to the nurse I refer to in my first book as 'Running Man.' He patiently explained, as I spelt it out, what I practically needed to do to wean myself off my tracheotomy, catheter and PEG feeding tube and how to learn the signs that would ensure that I made it to the loo in time for a number two! He also explained the processes that I would need to complete, in what order, to be discharged forever. He made me one step ahead and SMART.

Back then; there were days and weeks where I wasn't always so positive and focused. I would generally hide my really low moments from my close girlfriends by communicating to the nurses that I didn't want to see visitors. Instead, I would collapse into self-pitying tears in my bed alone. Was it a sign of weakness I wouldn't let my friends see? Or part of a natural grieving process for a life I had lost?

Most of the time, I was definitely a very difficult, headstrong patient who developed a level of impatience I'm not proud of. Timescales, to patients who live minute by minute by a clock on the wall, held medics and nurses to their promises. Whether that be a nappy change, nighttime drugs or the removal of a Trachi. I got really pissed off if things didn't happen as they had promised! They didn't and that bred my infuriation. It's also true we often didn't sing from the same hymn sheet, so to speak. Not withstanding that, my whole post-stroke experience was good.

However, it's important for me to add that I gave them back an unprecedented level of work ethic in return. (I am still very self-motivated.) They way I think of it, is that I'm a walking, talking CV of what can be achieved when a patient WANTS to be rehabilitated. I had the self-belief, the support and the positive anger to ensure that I kept fighting on every single day and the early intensive, therapy opportunity.

I certainly not only survived my crisis, I also thrived following it. Thankfully. I feel I can achieve even more in the future.

In the words of Rocky's famous, inspiring theme tune. I am...
'Gonna Fly Now!...'

'Kate, wake up.'
My eyes blinked open, blinded by the sun.
I came down to earth with a thump when Alison interrupted my daydreams with her relentless pestering

to play her favourite card game – predictive whist. You see, unlike her, I detested playing cards, but then again, I thought I did owe her big time!

Chapter 4 –
My Little Angels

When I first left hospital, for three months my kids were angelic. Fact.

They were really helpful, polite and considerate. They protected me from hearing their ensuing battles and, overall, seemed more settled now I was back home.

All my kids, (and Mark) would in turn, share my son's double bed on the first floor of our house. They would seem totally secure, as I would physically lie next to them. This rotation of 'musical beds' worked for our family, as all everyone wanted was to cuddle mum again and feel cocooned with my love. For me, to be tactile with the kids again was equally important as I watched them snooze and remember them as tiny babies. How could I have possibly known how their lives would be turned upside-down?

My jumpy, restless legs meant that I regularly left the rest of the family downstairs watching TV as I made my second journey on the stairs. I used to descend once in the mornings and ascend once at night. I quickly learnt that I would have to reduce the number of my treasured Earl Grey cuppas at 7pm each night because of my newly acquired bladder weakness. Less tea meant fewer disruptive nighttime shuffles to the loo.

I used to sit alone reading in front of my log burner in the kitchen, and take daily taxi journeys to the gym. I did feel a sense of liberation, if not a bit 'confined and institutionalised' at home.

My new non-working life was very different to my old one, as I sat and watched my child minder take on some of my 'mum' roles. She did all the jobs that I hated, from preparing packed lunches to ensuring the school reading and homework gets done and loading the dishwasher. All that said, she had 'replaced' me. I felt redundant.

Having me at home, like other 'normal' mums, was a sight no one ever expected, as they treated me with kid gloves.

That abnormally angelic behaviour all changed around the time I finished my first book in March 2011.

You see, just as I was working on my first stroke anniversary run, training myself to make it to the loo in time and re-training my bowels, (a bit like a toddler going from infantile to pre-schooler stage) I became aware that my little angels were changing before my very eyes. True, when I was in hospital, they endured the stuff of nightmares. Plus I smelt and looked weird and had tubes entering every orifice and vein. I was totally unable to give them any spoken or physical motherly reassurance then. Sure, I was their mum, but I bore no resemblance to the mum who had always juggled her role as businesswoman around their needs. They were not used to my absence. They had been, and still were, severely traumatised.

So at the time I struggled to find my feet as a full-time mum, whilst dealing with the legacy of a blood clot in my brainstem, they reverted to being 'normal' full-time little monsters!I have decided that kids have very short memories!

They had been used to my own mum's liberal and short-lived style of parenting in contrast to Mark's parents' child-rearing style, which consisted of rules, consistency and traditional love.

Where my mum was often seen buying them things as a bribe for good behaviour, Mark's mum would be trying to enforce a new behaviour chart. To be fair to her, she never went 'off timetable' with regards to the activities I would normally take them to and was well aware that sticking to my routine for the children was important in keeping some semblance of normality. Then there was my stepdad Dave, who only really knows how to parent like an army drill sergeant. I was totally unaware they had all been struggling in my unplanned, unprovoked absence.

On the edge of our new family life was Mark, who spent most of his day working or escaping the pressure cooker of home, by working in his office or visiting me. He didn't appear to spend much time with our kids and they knew it. So, it must have seemed both mum and dad were 'absent' to some extent.

Our kids' behaviour towards us became SO belligerent. I think it was due to separation anxiety and all the different 'mums and dads' swopping shifts at home. Our parents tried their hardest to be surrogate parents but they *were* grandparents and perceived in a different way. How could everyday home life seem normal?

The world, as India, Harvey and Woody saw it, must have felt as if it had been completely rocked. Added to their utter pain, trauma, vulnerability and almost non-existent parental unconditional love – they were alone dealing with their own trials and tribulations of life.

I fully accept that every family needs to protect their own kids, but we simply weren't able to defend or apologise for our kids' unruly behaviour back then. At that time, Mark and I were coping with my own life and death stuff. We had totally switched out of 'mum and dad mode' to focus on each new the issue of the day-all mine! I will never forget the battle with my pneumonia and having to deal with the worst constipation imaginable that left me doubled up in intense pain. The focus was all about getting my body healthy and functioning normally again.

Then there were all the extra demands of 'flip flowing' my catheter or pushing myself to achieve goals in rehab. What time *could* we allocate to the kids? Truthfully, their mum and dad had gone AWOL emotionally. They were confused and unguided, like little lost souls drifting out to sea and wondering why mum and dad could not hear their cries for help.

Even though Woody is very bright, loving and quite pivotal to my recovery at times, he had the worst tantrums ever. He had no shame or self control One day when Mark was away, I had to call Alison to the rescue, as he was wrecking his room and shouting some really hurtful stuff to me. My emotions and anxieties are all heightened post stroke so whilst he was only childishly lashing out verbally at me, he easily penetrated my 'mummy' force field so I felt every word like a stab to my heart.

So, with my head pathetically in my hands at the top of the second flight of stairs, Alison arrived, mid outburst, entering the bear-pit to act as referee. It seemed that Woody's uncontrollable, angry temper was simply because I'd not given him a five-minute warning to get off Club Penguin on his computer. A simple instruction I would have given in the past as a 'normal' Mum.

Alison sorted it, diffusing the war that had erupted, then hugged and reassured me, saying,

'Kate, you ARE getting there!'

Meanwhile, Harvey had become a stubborn middle-child who seemed to think he wasn't very special as he was neither the youngest or oldest child in the family. He wasn't violent but shouted all the time as he lazed on his Nintendo Xbox game or in front of the CBBC children's channel all night. Getting him to do any school reading was totally impossible, as was coaxing him to brush his teeth. I just didn't have either the physical or emotional strength to argue with him. So he carried on getting his own way, openly flouting every instruction I gave him. Harvey is very mature, self-confident, caring, sensitive and vulnerable but for a time he opted to display his aggressive, humorous, 'cheeky chappy' side.

As for India – always a very tactile, mature, kind and loving daughter – she had clearly been missing a female buddy in our otherwise 'male' house and her attitude was testing to say the least. India felt, ironically, that she was just as much 'Locked-in' as me.

She suffered emotionally and felt increasingly alienated and isolated during my spell in hospital. She believed it was totally unfair that she had to watch Harvey's football every week and feels Mark made no special 'dad and daughter' time for her.

India also stepped effortlessly into 'mini mum' mode, absorbing extra family responsibilities. She missed being able to confide in me and my affectionate hugs too and struggled to manage her awful skin condition. She couldn't remember the times Mark would take her out for coffee and cake and only recalled the times she felt like an outsider – the only female in the household overruled by the boys.

She used to hide her problems and protect me during our weekly visits, which were by no means easy for her. I now know she feels guilty that she couldn't see her mum more often in hospital, but, India, if I can adopt your expression, 'you should SO not!'

Earlier in 2011, the effects of my sustained family absenteeism, my new selfishness and pursuit of my charity escalated into a full-blown crisis when her hormones came out to bite me! She used to beat me into emotional submission with her speedily delivered excuses for any bad situation she found herself in or any reasonable (to me, anyway) telling off.

She was so tiring and untidy but probably only a very 'normal' 12-year-old girl! I couldn't respond nor could I argue back and I felt pummelled by her. She made the Little Britain fictional TV character Vicky Pollard (renowned for her fast-talking backchat) seem extremely harmless.

'Yeah but no but...' conflicts would develop, almost bi-hourly.

India was an early emotional developer anyway, but now was far older than her birth certificate would suggest or her other friends in terms of her having to grow up fast and leave some of her childhood by the wayside. She has coped with in enormous amount since 7th February 2010 with my long absence from home and also, when I returned to the family fold, with my multiple hospital emergency admissions since.

She may have hit her hormonal teens earlier than most, but she has always looked after me and responded to the copious emergencies with a level-headedness that belies her 12 years. Even though it's been challenging for us all, she has always been there for me.

India's outbursts were her way of expressing months of pent up anger at being 'different' from her peers and having a mum who had become debilitated by something out of her control. The stroke had stolen away her mum when perhaps she needed her most, and churned her emotions around. Early on, there were times she feared I was never coming out of hospital and she had to stay brave for the others.

It soon became blindingly obvious to me that all of my kids thought I hadn't been there for them which upset me greatly as my absence was through no fault of my own. I didn't *choose* to leave them. I was angry that my children didn't seem to realise I was finding family life such an enormous struggle.

Shouting out our anger became an outlet for all of us yet the kids won hands down. (Sorry neighbours!) I wasn't able to respond in my very weak voice or physically remove my kids from the volatile situations that would erupt daily.

Sad but brutally true, I even contemplated walking out on everyone because I'd become a liability and total failure as a mum. I convinced myself that I would be content in the knowledge that I would re-build our broken relationships in the future when I would be better able to cope and do them justice.

Thankfully, I never walked out then and I'm glad I didn't as I roughed it out. For now though, when things get really bad, I settle for sitting on my drive in my red, mini convertible, named Rocky, with my fingers in my ears whilst the stereo plays loudly, shouting at the top of my newfound voice.

'Blah, blah, blah....'

Interestingly, my kids lost all sense of any boundaries, and became mini hypochondriacs to boot!

You might wonder where Mark was?

Unfortunately, he was often away with work. However luckily for him he didn't have the pleasure of observing most of these daily wars. In a previous life, we would have given Woody the advanced warning he needed so he could manage his own anger issues or punish him by banning him from his favourite activities. With India, I would have known to immediately remove her mobile phone of Facebook for a week. Harvey's ban? It would have to be his much-loved football sessions, Xbox or TV.

I found that with me being almost eight months away, and with so many 'stand-in' mums and friends taking on my parental role, my little angels had changed beyond all recognition. To try and see it from my kids point of view, maybe, they actually felt unable to let themselves get too close to anyone after my stroke just in case they lost someone them?

I'm sure there must have been concerns about my motherly coping skills post hospital but we have all survived and somehow muddled through. I will always carry a large amount of blame and guilt for the 'family wars' that ensued then because I avoided conflict by seeking sanctuary in Facebook, Fighting Strokes, or the latest media promotion with my first book.

However I'm aware that my conflict avoidance exacerbated our family problems – which in turn perpetuated their low self-esteem, low confidence and lack of attention. I also know there is no such thing as the 'perfect' mum though I recognise the need to continue to make my own improvements but...I'm sure by now you are getting an insight into the high standards I set myself.

I hope my children will grow up to understand that life will have its lows and highs. My stroke experience has certainly taught them about coping with the unexpected.

In the words of Rocky Balboa,'*The world ain't all sunshine and rainbows.*'

Chapter 5 –
The Other Man In My life!

How did I find Mike? I had a major stroke of luck and please pardon the pun!

I had parked up in my 'new set of wheels' – well, NHS wheelchair actually, at Sheffield's Esporta gym (now a Virgin gym). I'd arrived with a business proposal for free gym membership in return for free PR. I was in marketing mode again and felt totally unfazed as I confidently thought I could sack the community stroke team and get everything working again myself! How deluded was I?

I pitched my idea to gym manager Alistair and took a deep breath. Alistair immediately dismissed my contra-deal. No, he was not interested in my deal. He gave a huge smile. I nervously smiled back. Was my idea that ridiculous? Funny even? A woman in a wheelchair wanting to run again when she could hardly walk? Perhaps it did seem laughable to anyone who did not feel my burning passion to achieve this goal. I suddenly felt deflated, but Alistair continued to talk.

He explained he wanted to offer his utmost support and was impressed with my chutzpah and had seen that it had taken me a lot of courage to ask for his help. He then offered his head physiotherapist and top personal trainer for free!

As meetings go, this one could not have gone better. The free gym sessions turned out to be the best way to spend my weekend hospital leave with Mark and our kids. I got fitter, as did they, and we enjoyed our 'normal' family time together. More importantly, they knew Mike was going to play an important role in my life.

I had all my family's emotional love and support but Mike had the expert's perspective on the gruelling series of physical challenges that lay ahead. There were quite simply loads of them but I knew I had to take one day at a time to accomplish them.

Mike proved to be a wonderful personal trainer and later became a trusted confidante. I could tell him anything. He knew how my mind worked. He was so organised, so thorough and truly professional. What he didn't know about the after effects of a brainstem stroke with Locked-in Syndrome, he quickly found out.

Now my whole family consider the gentle Cantonese man, with his far eastern deference and gentle manner, a true friend.

With the kids at school I could focus on my gym training. I arrived in a pre-booked taxi and always looked forward to getting out of my wheelchair and shaking off my 'disabled label'. I just wanted to be treated like any other gym-goer. I felt totally accepted and supported by everyone, partly due to Mike's welcoming positive attitude. Mike assured me he completely understood my obsession to run again.

Though he did turn pale when he learnt I wanted to run on the first anniversary of my stroke in Feb 2011, just three months away! He believed in me and I believed he could help me. He was, and still is, very unassuming and modest and has always shown total commitment to getting my body functioning properly and running again.

Mike worked on the basis that it wasn't all about 'if' certain muscles, like my ankle flex or my Gluteus Maximus, fired back into action – it was rather 'when'. Over the course of many months' training I would be building up my strength with electrical stimulation and learned repetitions and my muscles would work properly. I loved Mike's simple explanations and one-step-at-a-time approach to reaching our shared goals.

Mike can rest assured that since I left hospital, apart from six singing lessons, it's just been me and him, and what a team we've been!

He trained me like an athlete, which I liked, but he also gave me the confidence to walk unaided and to launch myself into a three stride run. Even though I was unable to time my opposite arms and legs in a march at the time! However much I've personally worked bloody hard, I've stayed with him for lengthy training periods and there's no denying it has TOTALLY been all about teamwork.

I'd often be seen asking some challenging recovery questions during our bi-weekly sessions. I wouldn't be exaggerating to say I could have easily written a neural physiotherapy research paper by now! Mike's unwavering commitment and belief in me and MY goals has been nothing short of AMAZING and defines what 'personal' training should be about!! I feel I am a person whose progress really matters to him. He, like Mark and Alison, should be awarded a medal for commitment.

I think you should read a potted history of what he has achieved with me. Here, with his kind permission, are his exact, unabridged notes.

Oct 2010
Patient arrives in wheelchair with limited movements of left side.
Strength and neuromuscular connectivity is apparent. Low weight and high repetitions implemented. Maximum support required to aid patient onto machines.

Nov 2010
Patient walked into gym with sticks. Her confidence has improved although still over relying on her right side. Continue to keep patient stable with machine weights and improving function dynamic movements. Moderate support required to aid patient onto machines.

Dec 2010
Patient now using cross trainer to increase cardio vascular efficiency. Patient independently walking up to 20m. lacking confidence, and self-belief. Due to having a small fall at home. Minimal support required to aid patient onto machines.

Jan 2011
Patient can now complete 15 mins on the cross-trainer with no problems. Patient walking up to 30m. Patient still has an antalgic gait, and does not want to load onto the left side. Limited ankle and hip movement and seems to stumble forward rather than load onto the left side.

Started work on core stability in supine laying and on a Swiss Ball.

Feb 2011
Weakness in hip flexors and no movement in left ankle in dorsiflexion and eversion. Kinesio tape applied to left rectus femoris, anterior tibialis and peroneus longus aid in muscular facilitation. Patient now confident to apply weight on to left side.
Patient completed 20m jog on the anniversary of her stroke. WELL DONE!
Mar 2011

Patient feels she needs a break after the 20m-jog event. Had 1 week of light exercise.
Working on single leg balance.
Patient started using the stair climber for 5 mins.
Went cycling for 30 mins outdoors. Patient application of balance to a bike is remarkable and shows neuromuscular connectivity and greatly improved.

Apr 2011
Working on eccentric loading of lat pulldown and leg press to gain more strength.
Patient achieved 30 min bike ride in Rother Valley whilst chatting to husband.
Also completed Nordic walking with walking polls.

Patient tired due to promotion of her first book. Has done a lot of traveling due to the media requesting interviews. Continued to work on core stability and joint stability. Patient jogged with support for 3x5m.

May 2011
Reverted back to the cross trainer. Competed 15 mins at level 6. Patient continues with Nordic walking and occasional bike ride. Single leg stability improving. Acupuncture and electrotherapy applied to improve up muscular contractions. Patient jogged with support for 3x10m. Jun 2011 Completed Nordic Walking for 40 mins Walked on treadmill at 4 kmh for 6 mins. Patient very tired this month and required acupuncture to help her sleep. Looking forward to her holiday in the USA.

Jul 2011
Back from holiday and motivated. Completed 4 days of cardio in a row at 30 mins each. She did a lot of walking when away and it is apparent that her strength and stability has paid off and has improved when she got back. Working on functional movement, lunges, squats, single leg squats, and rebound therapy. Patient jogged with support for 4x15m.

Aug 2011
15 mins stair climber and 10 mins cross trainer in one go. Strength improving nicely and ankle stability and strength in tibialis anterior and peroneal longus has much better control. Patient worked really hard on the stair climber and cross trainer this month. Patient jogged with support for 6x15m.

Sep 2011
Patient started to lift knees higher and ran 10m by her self until fatigue. However patient could not transfer the skill of lifting her left foot up when running.

Continued to work on single leg exercises and aiding patient with biomechanical advantages. Need to work on glutes to aid in applying power when running.

Oct 2011
Patient can run 6x20 m with 2 min rest in between. Also patient can run around an oval of 3x20 m. Worked on ballistic power and maximal muscular contractions until fatigued.

Nov 2011
Patient ran outside 60m in one go without rest. Cardio vascular and muscular fatigue is apparent.

In Mike's words...

'On 19 October, an anxious lady was wheeled into my consultation room. Being completely unaware of who Kate was and what she was able to do, it instantly reminded me of my hospital days when working on the Strokes Unit and with Spinal Cord injured patients. I asked her about her past medical history and I couldn't believe what she has been through since February 2010. After hearing that she had Locked-in Syndrome, and being told that she would be in a nursing home for the rest of her life, I really felt for her, especially when she hasn't had the opportunity to try and get her life back. I can remember as if it was yesterday when I asked her what she expected from me and what she wanted to do. She replied with her slurred speech, "I want to be normal and I want to run by the anniversary of her stroke". I almost laughed under my breath, not because it was impossible, but because she was a very ambitious lady and I thought her goals were not only unrealistic but I knew no one had ever achieved this. When I was in the hospitals I knew that many minor stroke patients only regained walking with walking aids by least 1 or maybe 2 year post incident, but with Kate who had severe stroke and Locked-in Syndrome this lady wants to independently run within a year! I replied, "I can't promise you anything, but in order to get you where you want to be, it's going to be hard work." Although I had never rehabilitated any patient to running within a year I knew my current knowledge and the amount of time I could spend with her was a massive advantage to when I worked in the hospitals.

So I set off to assess her and found that she pretty much had no upper or lower limb function to her left side. It was going to be hard work when she said that Calendar News would be at her 1-year anniversary event and I started to sweat. I felt the great pressure of needing to achieve her goals, and deep inside I knew there was a possibility that we wouldn't get anywhere near what we have set out. As I saw her twice a week I got to know Kate as a person. To me, she was very strong-minded and that was a great help as most patients who see me rely on my motivation to get them to there goals. I used this to my advantage and I pushed her beyond her limits in terms of training because I knew she wanted to be normal so badly. She has that Gung Ho mentality, and by all means I believe it is the right mentality as she has nothing to lose and everything to gain! As you may know she was out of her wheelchair and onto sticks within 8 weeks and then was walking independently by Christmas 2010. Through her hard work and my guidance we achieved something special as she also completed her first 20-metre jog on the anniversary of her stroke. We have now set out for greater heights as we start the Percy Pud training and aim for Kate to achieve a 1km run. I will continue to push the boundaries of her ability through the application of sports science and physiotherapy and I look forward to December when we run together and complete an event no other stroke victim has achieved throughout history. Her passion for success is reflected in what she has already achieved. She carries her hard work into her charity for raising the awareness of stroke in young adults. As a practitioner I have learnt so much about Kate, and whenever I see her I know that anything is possible when you put your mind to it. I also share the same passion with Kate as my company continues to support her charity through sponsored runs and charity events. It has been a pleasure to work with Kate and I hope our story truly inspires readers to follow their goals and chase their dreams.'

So, Mike helped me achieve my goal to run (actually shuffle) by my stroke date's first anniversary. He got me into a proper running style to run/walk/run 1 kilometre of the Percy Pud, 10km race on 4/12/12. Around six weeks before that race, I was asked to write a running blog for 'The Running Bug', so this is what I wrote...

12.10.11 Gonna Fly Now!
It's Wednesday 12th October, with the Percy Pud 10km road race on the 4th December in Sheffield. I am only running 500 metres (with stops), inside now. How on earth am I going to achieve the 1km as the race starter, in aid of my Fighting Strokes charity by then?

My personal trainer is extremely confident that I will do it. (After all, in one year since I left hospital, where I was for 8 months, he has got me out of a wheelchair, off sticks, walking, running on the first anniversary of my brainstem stroke with Locked-in Syndrome. Although, the running style wasn't pretty!) So why should I not believe him now? (It was self-belief and bloody hard work that has got me here so far!) The Rocky theme tune, Gonna Fly Now by Bill Conti, is playing on my iPhone ringtone, rousing me and forcing me into action. I have a strong word with myself, whilst thinking 'the steps scene' as Sylvester Stallone famously punches the air. (In fact the inspiration behind our FightingStrokes.org charity logo.) But has fatigue and possibly over training after the last 18 months since my stroke stifled my commitment to my training regime? Mike won't let me back off with all the arduous lunges, stepper machine, inside shuttle runs, leaps, stretching, acupuncture and functional electric stimulation today. In my free time, (I see my gym work as a job!) I love nothing more than to relive my old fell running days, as I pursue Nordic Walking in the Peak District instead. Stomping in between the trees out in the Peak District was reminiscent of me starting my running career running in between lampposts in and around Sheffield. Maybe the space, scenery, time to reflect is what I need to get back on track? My book – 'Running Free' (Amazon) epitomises the freedom of running for me, I'm told that when one masters the Nordic Walking technique, it feels like you are 'Gonna Fly Now!'

19.10.11 My Epiphany Moment!

I've had an epiphany moment! I have decided to take a 3-month sabbatical from my charity Fighting Strokes after working so hard all year, whilst still recovering from my brainstem stroke symptoms. A day being directionless and lost, made me come to the decision the time is right to write my story as I see it, over the last year since leaving hospital. The distraction and focus is so important for my peace of mind and it became apparent that apart from enjoying my own company that I just simply don't know how to do nothing and just train for my 1 km! But its training you want to hear, so, I've had a week of acupuncture, kinesiology and my first 80 yard outdoor scuttle in the gym car park!

The acupuncture to release my left leg muscles, especially around my hip and ankle (because of foot drop tiredness) but also to ensure that I have lots of great nights of sleep! The Kinesiology was new. I must admit I am a little sceptic, but I was of acupuncture and that has helped, so why not give this a go! Here's the science bit, kinesiology addresses physiological, mechanical, and psychological mechanisms. Kinesiology can be applied to human health in these ways: biomechanics and orthopaedics, rehabilitation such as physical and occupational therapy, as well as sport and exercise. Studies of human and animal motion include measures from motion tracking systems, electrophysiology of muscle and brain activity, various methods for monitoring physiological function, and other behavioural and cognitive research techniques. Can this approach really help what has been functional and physiological damage caused by my stroke? Are kinesiology methods useful in unlocking my hip flexors and ankle muscles to allow me to run further before tiring? I don't know, but my personal trainer thought my gait had improved and I certainly felt that my muscles had been worked. But is it a temporary or long-term fix?

So all this theory and practise plus an 80-yard dash, up a hill, in the car park. Lungs were ok; legs wobbly, but I did it! Coming down hill was easier, so all stuff to build on. The session today finished with my personal trainer making me left leg lunge to a wobbly cushion. Hopefully, this will improve my stability when I run.

Half Term October 2011

My gym training is pretty much on hold with half term and my fulltime childcare. I've had to make do with lots of walks to the Rec, and only the odd brief session at the gym, (when my best mate can occupy my youngest son, Woody). I've settled for biking on my exercise bike, in the playroom, at home.

Cardio vascular wise I'm OK but my core stability is dodgy. My hip strength exercises are my priorities, to build my stamina for my 1km race. But, can I survive without:
a) Mike (my personal trainer) for a week? And
b) The full charge of my three delightful kids?... And
c) Jeremy Kyle?

I know I'm probably one of many thousands of women who secretly love watching a bit of Jeremy Kyle but it's not overly motivating programme to watch on an exercise bike at home! (I picked up this habit during my long, incarceration in hospital, though I'm not proud to admit this.) So I'm using Mr Kyle as a replacement to Mike. When I just can't tolerate any more of the show's DNA tests results any more, I play my rousing ringtone on my IPhone, which happens to be the Rocky theme tune, aptly called, 'Gonna Fly Now.'

I drift away as I clock the miles up. I think how I really still miss the fells, the girly banter, the fresh air, and space from when I used to run regularly for 20 miles or more, in the stunning Peak District. Ok, so you could say that it was my guilty, selfish pleasure. (A bit like Mr Kyle or my bi-annual Sausage and Egg McMuffin at McDonalds!) I'm sure I'll survive refereeing my kids for the week; even if I have to do more playroom leg raises and lunges over a wobble cushion to be able to escape!

1.11.11 Gonna Fly Now!

It may have been the Rocky theme tune but it was now playing loud and clear in my head, as I took my first, outdoor running steps! Metaphorically, I punched the air, like Rocky on those famous steps in the film while I beamed a broad smile of relief at my achievement. It was in the salubrious location of the gym car park, on an autumnal day, where I took three deep breaths, then put into practise my many months of lunges, wobble board, inside shuttle runs and the step machine exercises.

I actually had forward, as opposed to upward momentum and surprisingly a bit of speed.

As Mike took the photo's I took my life into my own hands as I ran with no chaperone. I bloody well did it and it actually felt easier than a week ago, so maybe all my hard work had paid off over half term after all.

My aim was 100 yards before tiring. I actually managed 70 yards. My lungs were burning, as I was unable to breath in enough air for my short burst of exertion, but my left foot predictably and suddenly dropped, preventing me from reaching my goal .Not great news given that I have exactly one month to go before the Percy Pud race! Back to the hard work tomorrow....

10.11.11 Now... I'll take all the help you can give!

33 days of training to go! Mike is pulling out all the stops. Sure I can run 100 yards four times with 30 seconds rest in between, but 1km by 4th, really?

I think I may have bitten off more that even I can chew, this time. My lungs are actually feeling like they are going to explode after 100 yards, shocking to think, when I could once run 25 miles in one session easily and walk up hills!

4.12.11 (The Percy Pud Race)

It couldn't have been a fouler day. The horizontal wind and rain and OH so cold! 1,600 of us competitive and non-competitive runners assembled to run and complete the famous Yorkshire 10km race in return for a Christmas pudding.

Armed with 15 of my Fighting Strokes supporters, husband, kids, best friend and physiotherapist, I lined up. At 9.30am the race gun fired and we were off. The front runners were so tall, lean and fast! They practically sprinted for the whole race. My speed was a little more than a stop-start, but it was a running style and it was a forward momentum. Even though I resembled a trotting horse!

It felt good, as I was able to show off my newfound skills to my pals. After what seemed like 500 metres, I was shattered and motioned to my trainer to return back to complete the remaining 500 metres over the large finish line. However, just as we pulled up alongside a bus stop we noticed the 9km race marker sign. Unbeknown to any of us, we had actually run 1km. I was elated with the biggest grin. I'd done it!

We doubled back after a quick celebratory photo from the nice man at www.flamingphotography.co.uk who just happened to be on the right spot on the road!

I crossed the finish line and actually ran/walked for 1.5km shattered, happy, hugely relieved but very cold. I then spoke live on air to Radio Sheffield's Rony Robinson (and Fighting Strokes patron) and enjoyed a warm cup of coffee before I was presented with my own silver cup by race director in the marquee by Richard Dunk, who said, 'We have a very special trophy for a very special person, ladies and gentlemen, if you'll show a round of applause for Kate Allatt. All of us at the Steel City Striders Running Club, and me, as race director of the Percy Pud 10k are proud that Kate picked our race as her goal and challenge to get her back on the fitness trail and back to full health. Well done Kate!'

My friends will have raised more than £1000 for Fighting Strokes – they were there to support me yet again. Even my best mate Alison who 'didnt' do running' was at my side throughout. Best of all, is that I had a goal to run again and lose my wheelchair, way back in Osborne 4 in 2010 and I've bloody done it!

All In A Pud Cause! Thanks for believing in me Mike.

The Percy Pud 4 December 2011 me and Mike Lee.

© www.flamingphotography.co.uk

Chapter 6 –
Budgie Smugglers!

'I'm so irresistible!'

Mr. Guest was calling to us by the pool and he wanted an audience.

'You watch!'

Us girls looked up to see what antics Mr. Guest would be getting up to next. Since we had met him, he was turning out to be quite a character. Was that a comedic twinkle in his eye or the sunlight reflected from the swimming pool? What was he up to now?

Before we had the time to quash his self-belief in his Adonis- like qualities, the hilarious holidaymaker 'paraded himself' around the pool in his Budgie Smugglers – a term the media coined for Daniel Craig's ultra-tight swimming trunks worn in 'Casino Royale'.

Mr. Guest was certainly no Bond as he oozed little mystery and did not have the pecs or toned abs. Yet, as he strutted around the poolside, secretly counting each female admirer, you had to give him credit for not taking life, or himself, too seriously. It transpired this Essex Man With A Tan was a solicitor who sincerely thought that all the women fancied him and found his briefest of briefs interesting. We couldn't help but warm to him and his innocent poolside banter.

When his antics were over, it was very evident that he had been pretty pleased with his humorous performance. Amazingly, he attracted over twenty 'admirers', which had he duly added up. We were quick to point out that this figure was reflection of puzzled sun worshippers wondering what on earth he was doing walking around in a silly posturing manner. NOT because they were entranced by his charm and charisma.

As he settled down on his sun lounger and proceeded to chat in a teasing manner, we soon realized the jury may have been out as regards to his female magnetism – but he was certainly fun to be around. If you wanted a laugh-a-minute holiday entertainer, he was most definitely your man.

Mr Guest's wife, (as well as our husbands, Mark, Chris, James and Bill) should be aware it was all innocent light-hearted fun. Of course, our middle-aged friend was not seriously being flirtatious with us. We think he was perceptive enough to somehow know we needed to let our hair down, recuperate and enjoy ourselves. He joked he wore the Budgie Smugglers to improve his tan-lines. Though Mr Guest, it seemed, was not into sunbathing.

Not satisfied with his own brand of entertainment, the pool prankster proposed boys versus girls informal volleyball match. I took up the rear guard position where less of the action would be, although hadn't again thought through the 'how' I was going to actually play volleyball. I was stronger on my feet now, but unable to jump or quickly respond to a punched ball flying in my direction. I was useless. It was fair to say and I was increasingly becoming a liability, as the boys slaughtered us.

Jaq and I were competitive and my growing inability to participate properly in the game prompted me to become a volunteer to become the referee. Alison did pretty well considering her arthritic, painful joints but Anita (usually incredibly agile) was just so uncoordinated. It had been more like four versus two as Jaqui leapt around athletically taking and receiving almost every shot, from the other team. The imbalanced teams were then mixed up. I quickly figured that I couldn't meaningfully participate in the volleyball game, but I sure as hell was going to make my mark on this event by being an 'unfair' referee. My deliberately, biased decisions riled the always extremely impartial Jaqui.

I had no shame in helping the underdog team win. She hammed up her protests in response to my dubious line calls. In the end, however much I tried to scupper things, Jaqui and Mr. Guest's team won the match! I bowed out gracefully in defeat. After all, we had all had a great time thanks to our new friend's exuberant fun character. Too bad I was incommunicado. In the space of a few hours, our new budgie smuggling friend had given me plenty to tweet about!

Chapter 7 –
No Credits Left!

Mark's parents took charge of the children during my three nights away in Majorca. Ann and Kev were always so reliable and consistent and ensured that the kids did their homework and, if needed, were disciplined. I'd particularly specified that the kids should continue to eat wholesome food with fresh vegetables and everyone agreed it was best to leave the kids daily routine unchanged. They reassured me they would stick to my 'to do list' and I felt quite chilled leaving the children knowing I had such supportive In Loco Parentis In-Laws.

I had come a long way from how I felt exactly a year ago and was SO ready for a break!

For the record, I have always maintained my utmost gratitude to all the support I have received from Mark, Alison, Anita and Jaqui when it came to ensuring my kids' lives were kept as normal as possible. Not forgetting the excellent surrogate parental roles played by my in-laws Ann and Kev and my mum Jan and stepdad Dave.

However, when I left hospital I did become increasingly depressed. I felt very unworthy at times as my self-esteem plummeted.

Often my paranoia, level of anger and irritability (a classic stroke legacy) was disproportionate to any 'incidents', which occurred daily. These behavioural manifestations demonstrated my inability to control my feelings. I only rake this up now, because it may help other stroke survivors' family and friends understand their behaviour and prepare them for a future with a person who has undeniably changed in character. Perhaps they will be able to understand some of the reasons for their loved ones' unexplained aggression. I certainly felt aggressive and I know this shocked those around me. It was how I truly felt at the time.

There were also uncontrollable bouts of laughing when I was actually angry, which my kids understandably found totally confusing. Hence, why I had to introduce the 'T' sign for timeout, when my kids misbehaved, so they knew that my escalating laughter wasn't comedic. When my ever-increasing anger erupted as loud laughter, I must have seemed like a crazy pantomime villainess such was my theatrical laughter that was more frightening than funny.

Since I left hospital, my closest friend's support remained. Alison became my Fighting Strokes charity secretary and Jaqui my chairwoman. I felt extremely privileged to have such great friends. Anita joined me on my weekly walk on Blacka Moor, (stunning moorland to the west of Sheffield) and we always returned feeling invigorated and refreshed.

Nevertheless, I was quite upset with my relatives back then even though it may have seemed I had everything to be happy about. Don't get me wrong, I felt so happy when I first walked out of hospital with my mum on Wednesday 29th September 2010.

It was a euphoric moment in my life and captured forever on a video, which can be seen at 'Runmadkate', on my YouTube channel. We went straight to the local Cricket Inn pub for a celebratory 'freedom' lunch. I had escaped into the world again!

Back at the Allatt household, India, Harvey and Woody had created 'Welcome Home' banners and posters and there was a temporary wheelchair ramp outside my house. Once through the door, I breathed in all the sights, sounds and smells of 'home.' I experienced the inexplicable feeling of belonging somewhere safe and secure other than a hospital room. As my family and friends embraced me I felt enveloped in love and heady memories of life before my stroke. The whole family had longed for this moment and it was one none of us expected to experience, so we savoured it. Even with the added array of eight months' clutter around my house, it felt great to be home. Later, Mark's parents (staying overnight as Mark was working away) cooked my favourite roast lamb dinner complete with Yorkshire Puddings!

I know both sets of parents were enormously anxious about me coming home. They thought about the weight of responsibility on their non-medical shoulders. Just like the time I was in Osborne 4, I wasn't easy to help. In retrospect, I probably didn't seem grateful. It was tough being back, but back as a different person who needed looking after. I presume it was a bit like having a having a fourth child around, albeit one who needed extra care and attention.

They needed to know where I was going, or what I was doing at all times. Someone was on 24-hour watch in those early weeks.

Regardless of my premature hospital discharge, I was still very, very poorly. I was definitely in denial about my health. Big time.

You see, in my mind I felt that I'd come so far already, compared to those graphic images of me in ICU, so I hated being treated as though I was 'needy'. Given I was discharged, surely I was nearly 'normal,' wasn't I?

Wrong!

But the truth is, I was very deprived – very disabled – or in other words not 'able' to do very much at all! I sat on my bar stool or my new red upholstered chair in the kitchen and walked gingerly with my Zimmer frame. The fact, I alone was responsible for turning it into a 'go-faster' model was an extra challenge but I would have lost the (poshly named) Buckingham Caddy – the integrated tray in which to put all your bits 'n' bobs and gone for the lower spec! It was far too heavy on the corners!

As you can see, I can joke now – but my life was very tough in those early months after my hospital discharge and I was still working on improving my speech too. I wasn't prepared for any of those hurdles. Nor did I take any medicine to ease my symptoms or emotional 'downs' except from my daily child's dose of Aspirin, Cod Liver Oil capsules, Omega 3, 6 and 9 and Zinc supplements.

From around 7pm each night, I suffered with chronic jumpy or restless legs. It was also clear to everyone that my ability to swear had not been impaired, especially in front of the kids – not good!

It was round that time that I also discovered my unreliable swallow reflex. I don't mean that food went down my windpipe, but I was often unable to squeeze food down my oesophagus. (Other chapters explain this well!)

I had developed awful mood swings, which were both distressing and upsetting for my loved-ones to observe. Interestingly, I only ever cancelled Mike, my personal trainer, five times in the 18 months I had been seeing him. On 'down days', I just couldn't bear to get up or leave the house. It would be wrong to suggest that I left hospital and there was an upward line on a graph of happiness. It was more like a jagged up and down line and I was struggling to make sense of my changing mindset. After all, as everyone kept telling me, I had made such terrific progress, right?

Over my many days alone at home absorbed in a book in front of a log fire, I would continually analyse all the physical and emotional injustices that I felt I'd suffered in hospital. You could say that I had too much time to dwell and fester. I'm not proud to say it, but I was becoming bitter. That was something Alison, especially, never wanted to happen.

I would, in my mind, re-play the 'lowlights' of my post stroke life story, which for some unfathomable reason seemed to overshadow the many highlights and major achievements so far. It was my positivity, fuelled by my anger, which helped me recover so why had negative thoughts now invaded my mind?

I replayed my angry triggers over and over in my mind. There was my first premature and traumatic review in Osborne 4; the injustices of my family's first trip to Cornwall without me over my 40th birthday; my own mother's disappearance for a three week holiday to America over my birthday, which signalled to me her apparent 'no confidence' in my ability to recover. Either that, or she was getting on with her life because medical staff had told her they expected me to remain crippled for the rest of my life or she was knackered; my family's second Cornwall holiday, again without me; Mark selling MY car without warning me (and telling our kids not to say anything); the power of attorney/Will incident in ICU, etc. These injustices once fuelled my desire to bloody well show everyone they were wrong and not to write me off, but now I could no longer draw on my fury to stop my uncharacteristically depressive thoughts taking root.

I was going into self-destruct with depressing downward spiralling thoughts. I felt so alone again. In my mind I continued to feel as terribly unworthy, as I did in hospital and certainly undeserving of any kind friends. In truth, I also began to feel guilty for my 'neediness' and over reliance on Alison and my latterly my long-suffering charity trustees. Alison understood I had always been proud of being Capable Kate (Even though she thought my worries of being too needy were ridiculous at the time).

Did I ever think of taking anti-depressants or having therapy? No way, I was strong, wasn't I? I was always trying to prove to others of my superhuman qualities on Facebook, as well as trying to convince myself.

Besides, I'd spent eight months consuming, via my PEG, a cocktail of drugs administered by the ICU and rehabilitation nurses and once-a-week psychologist, whose relaxation CD, I'd hidden.

I was not into New Age type music. How could it help me relax if it just irritated me? In hospital I showed my disdain for the CD in no uncertain terms.

I communicated to friends to hide the twinkly ocean wave music. I had a hole from my tracheotomy, not a blowhole. Perhaps as well as suffering from a major stroke doctors thought I had morphed into a b***** dolphin! I much preferred listening to The Smiths. (Though perhaps 'Girlfriend in a Coma' may not have been on my preferred playlist!)

Yet no one had asked me what music I wanted to listen to? It was a case of treating ALL patients the same. It seemed health carers know best. It was a one type-of-music-fits-all approach, which only got my back up. I was an individual with likes, dislikes and preferences, not just another stroke patient who needs to listen to NHS prescribed easy listening music – the most inane and annoying soundtrack imaginable!

How on earth could it be of benefit? Listening to crashing waves and dolphin/whale noises are fine if you are on an expensive whale-watching expedition in Iceland or off the Cornish coast. You can appreciate the real experience. If you are trapped in a sanitised hospital, such noises only remind you of what wonders of the Natural World are beyond your grasp.

Back home I did chill out during my many 'Morrissey Moments'.

I can appreciate the irony of Morrissey's 'I Am Two People.'

I have two faces
One of which you know
The other one
For your sake
I never would show.

Apt lyrics indeed. Yes, Morrissey could have been singing about me! I kept everything inside about how I was feeling. I saw it as a weakness to let people know when I felt down. After all, I was Kate The Stroke Survivor and in the words of Mary Poppins, still felt I had to be 'Practically Perfect In Every Way.' I had always felt like this but now, post stroke, it just felt harder as I put so much extra pressure on myself.

Outsiders wanted to see my life as the happy ending, not the sad beginning of a new post stroke life. I became very socially withdrawn and still am to a certain extent. I found a new best friend during those long, quiet winter days in the form of my red netbook where I kept up the façade that everything was tickety-boo. I deserved a BAFTA! (when you get to read my acknowledgements, you'll probably think I'm up for an Oscar too!)

At that time, a child minder collected the kids, so I never got to see, let alone chat to or gossip with the other mums. I had no job, so I was pretty worthless to society wasn't I?

Sure, on my 'Beatinglockedinsyndrome' page on Facebook, I was the confident extrovert, chatting about my latest mobility progress with Mike, but these status updates meant I could avoid on my negative anxieties.

I was unique, wasn't I? Whether I was unique or not, I certainly felt very alone and totally misunderstood in my new world. I wanted to project my positive progressions, which I hope wasn't seen as deliberately misleading my cyber friends in any way. My life wasn't a bed of roses, but complaining about it endlessly sure as hell wasn't going to help me get better. Most people's lives have difficulties. Mine was no different. Was it?

I didn't think it would help my demons, if I openly shared my new life anxieties or discussed every single medical affliction I'd acquired since my stroke. I certainly didn't think it would helpful to me nor interesting nor would it be uplifting to any other stroke survivors.

It won't surprise you when I say that I became a prolific Facebook, Twitter and Text user. I became addicted to social media, because it projected my 'normality'. It also made me generally focus on the positive steps in my recovery in my status update, as opposed to my newfound afflictions, routines or physical weaknesses. I got positive affirmation and encouragement from my followers, which fired my desire to improve, surprise and humour people. With my increasingly tough home life, social media gave me temporary respite from my personal misery.

My insomnia, (which Mike has latterly corrected with acupuncture), helplessness, increasingly challenging kids and an inability to enjoy any pleasure (the medical term is Anhedonia), made for a pretty depressing existence back then. During this time, Alison, would let herself into my house via my external 'key safe' for a Caffe latte, to try and do her best to limit my solitary boredom.

I lost the ability to gulp drinks down or inhale and hold deep breaths. I remember how I was always proud to swim a whole length underwater with just one breath before my stroke, but now I could only swim three metres.

So how mobile was I? Once a day, with Mark's assistance, I was able to shuffle upstairs to go to bed and then once a day to descend downstairs for breakfast. Fortunately, I've got a downstairs loo, which was a place I often suffered embarrassing accidents, a bit like a toddler would do as they transition to a pre-schooler.

When I had my bowel movements, they weren't just an 'every-other-day' worry, but an obsession. I had to plan where every toilet on every journey was to avoid panic. Isn't that both a toddler and an old-age thing? After all there's nothing worse than wetting yourself in public...or doing the 'other' far from the safety of home. Memories of an embarrassing infant school assembly 'incident' came back to haunt me on every search for a 'ladies loo' direction symbol. I was a grown-up but felt like I was potty-training all over again. When I was first in nappies, I did not like Mark seeing me this way, as I did not feel feminine or attractive.

Mark totally understood my worries about getting to the 'ladies' on time when out and about and proved to be a tower of strength during these embarrassing times, which thankfully are over. I suppose you can describe these feelings as those experienced by women when they first give birth who often worry that their husbands might see them differently forever more.

I woke up very early most mornings, probably my hospital institutionalisation. I also had wide-awake daily nightmares where I wasn't in fact in my kitchen but staring from my hospital bed, totally paralysed. I'd quickly end the daytime nightmare, which I know is some sort of post traumatic stress, by literally pinching myself back to planet earth.

The other re-occurring panic attack was that I would catch pneumonia and die.

So much so, that I made an appointment to see my doctor for reassurance. She said, 'It is unlikely to happen to you now that you are mobile.'

I used to think of the worst-case scenarios.

'You watch, I'll get bloody pneumonia and suddenly die, so all this bloody hard work would have been wasted after all!'

An index finger would have felled me like an aging tree, I was that weak. My legs wobbled inside continuously, as though they struggled to keep me standing upright. I felt as if they were missing the scaffolding that held my skin and muscles up.

So, on the one side, I was trying to project my 'normalness' to everyone – which I now understand had made it hard for my family to know how to help me back at home. On the other side, I had a secret mix of traumas, worries, anxieties and extreme physical limitations that nobody knew about. I'd left hospital, so obviously I was no longer needy right?

I always wanted to be Rocky, inside and out. But there were times, despite my fightback; I was a lonely and emotional less. If I were someone he was pummelling in the boxing ring, I would undoubtedly have been the loser. At that time, no way would I have been the victorious champ holding a fist high in the air – the image of myself I so often played in my mind. If Rocky had walked into my life and asked me: 'How You Doin?' I would have replied, 'Not so good!'

During my incredibly low times, I used to muse how come it was Mark who had received all the family help with the kids, while I lay in hospital, (which obviously, indirectly helped me too). I couldn't comprehend why, when I left hospital, all that family help quickly stopped? We all cope differently and can handle all sorts of levels of 'difficulty'. The word 'difficulty' is something we all experience but it's a relative word. For example, a divorce, with kids involved is difficult, if that's the worst thing that has happened to you in your life. As is fighting cancer, dealing with the death of a loved-one or work-related stress. In similar situations why do some people thrive, yet others can't cope?

Don't misunderstand me. I was enormously grateful that my kids' grandparents trailed to Sheffield every single week to act as surrogate parents. However, I began to feel very unworthy and lonely when they returned to their homes and lives in the autumn of 2010.

I used to think that Mark had somehow bloody well used up all the grandparents' goodwill. At a time when I felt others thought I was breezing along in my new role back home, I was actually out of my comfort zone once they had left. At the time, when I felt isolated and vulnerable, it seemed there were no credits left!

Unbeknown to me, until January 2011, Ann and Kev were privately funding part of my child minder remotely from their Southport home. But my mum and dad were completely off the scene in pursuit of all the stuff they did before my illness. I know their everyday lives had stressfully been suspended due to my unforeseen stroke circumstances but I did not anticipate their lives would 'resume as normal' in the way they seemingly did. The cause of my illness wasn't my fault either but I often felt that's the way it was perceived.

At the time it happened, yes, I was pretty stressed as I was establishing my new digital marketing business. I also was very fit. Perhaps, too fit? I was an extremely hard working Mum, (probably only an average wife), who loved to sledge on the Peak District slopes, with my kids. But I certainly wasn't a bad person or cavalier as I approached middle age.

Perhaps, Mark should have set up paid childcare arrangements sooner? This would have taken the pressure off the grandparents and would have left him with some 'help' credits when I came home? His decisiveness would have also allowed both families to remain the 'spoiling grand parents' and not seemingly the 'baddy' surrogate mum and dad?

Had they had used up all used up their coping abilities? Most definitely. Did they need to pick up the reins of their old lives? Probably. Was that understandable back then? Absolutely not, but time has most definitely softened me.

In pursuit of 'normalness' at home, Mark never missed a day's work, but did my relatives see it as some sort of inequality in the grandparents' love or support for their other grandchildren? Perhaps, but I'll never know.

Either way, rightly or wrongly, I was feeling emotionally wounded when I came home. We all dealt with my illness in different ways and still do, in fairness to them, or me, there was no such thing as a 'manual' on how to cope.

I repeat that, 'some people thrive and some can't cope.'

I unfairly expected my family and friends to become mind readers, just like they'd been in the early weeks of my stay in ICU, but they clearly weren't now. Consequently, I was very lonely and physically withdrawn, as I struggled to say the right thing with people and integrate into 'normal' Dore life. My life consisted of books and daily workouts with Mike.

My complex emotions, coupled with the laborious and mentally exhausting process of writing 'Running Free', was a far more involved process than I could have imagined. The stark facts, when written down, served only to remind me that I had been through a lot of turmoil. I was ready for a bit of light relief.

Chapter 8 –
Media, Mirth and Merriment

I was going through a particularly tough month of wallowing, bought on by re-living the ICU experiences for my first book (completed in just five months after leaving hospital). Fortunately, unflappable Alison was on hand to keep my spirits up.

Tuesday April 12th 2011 was going to be fun, fun, and more fun!

Alison was helping me combine my book promotion with an adventurous trip to London. With copies of 'Running Free' in my bag and all my business paraphernalia, notes and essential items carefully packed in my laptop bag; I was on a marketing mission with a difference.

The taxi arrived at my house at 5.55am ready to take us on the 15-minute journey from Dore to Sheffield, where we were booked on the 6.30am train to St Pancras International. We had already spent days getting into a giddy frenzy, planning our timetable. We also joked we may also do some celeb spotting during our visit to our wonderful capital.

The reason? I was going to be interviewed by Jeremy Vine on his BBC Radio Two show. I was no longer the mute listener; I was going to highlight the issues that concern Locked-in stroke survivors, and was looking forward to being an individual with something important to say.

After my scheduled interview, I was launching 'Running Free' at the world famous London Book Fair which had opened the previous day at Earls Court.

We were glammed up, with straightened hair and fully manicured nails (though Alison's always are) and felt more than ready for our city adventure. Until that point, wearing any eye make-up for me was sporadic, and I was unable to apply my once trusty black, liquid eyeliner, let alone mascara without smudging it over my eyes and nose.

Not a good look! Yet I managed to somehow 'put my face on' to face the world and even felt quite business-like again. I was determined to show people that just because I had a stroke didn't mean I was incapable of holding a decent conversation. My speech may not have been completely 'normal' at this stage but to be honest I did not worry too much that morning, as I was so excited to be meeting the fabulous Jeremy Vine as guest on his show.

It is no secret I am a real fan of the Jeremy Vine show on BBC Radio Two. In fact his show became a great comfort to me when I was at my lowest. The mixture of topical debates and music kept my spirits up got my mind into gear again. Plus the most interesting guests seem to be on his morning show and Jeremy's no-nonsense interview style, warmth and sincerity make you feel he has the uncanny knack (honed skill?) of making you feel you have known him all your life.

How did I manage to be booked for Jeremy Vine's show? I'd only had the national radio exposure because of a recent 'drunk' school reunion curry night in Macclesfield. (I only had one glass!)

During dinner, my good friend Mrs Gowing kindly offered her sister's services to secure a meeting with her employers, BBC Radio 2. It was an excellent opportunity to promote my book and charity.

Suited and booted in my short monochrome 'business' dress, with black leggings, I exited the taxi at Sheffield railway station with a sense of anticipation of the day ahead. Alison and I stocked up on yoghurt, croissants, skinny lattes and glossy magazines and once aboard the train I thought I'd better phone my co-writer, who was already in London.

We just needed to inform her that we had indeed boarded the train and our estimated time of arrival. After all, the media works to set deadlines and we knew we weren't to be late.

Patiently waiting for my Iphone signal, we tucked into our takeaway breakfasts and just as I was writing my text, Alison (in typical giddy, mischievousness fashion), snatched my Iphone and deleted my message mid-text

*Before my stroke, I was a keen fell
runner/competitive road runner.*
© Kate Allatt

Family Fun in Cyprus, May 2009. © Kate Allatt

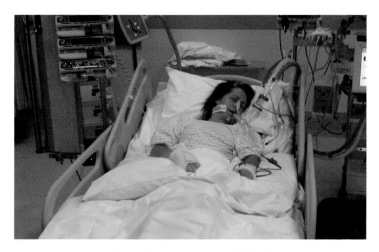

Is that really me? 7th February 2010 HDU Northern General Hospital Sheffield. I'm wired to a life support machine with breathing tube after my catastrophic brainstem stroke with Locked -In Syndrome. © Kate Allatt

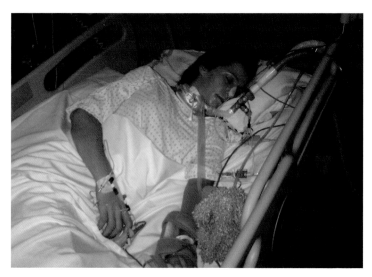

Two weeks later. I am fitted with Tracheotomy, stomach feeding tube and catheter with arm and foot splints...and cuddly toy! © Kate Allatt

Happy smiles from Alison and me on the infamous Sheffield to London train journey to meet Jeremy Vine, April 2011.
© Kate Allatt

I meet Mr. Jeremy Vine at BBC Radio 2 on Tuesday April 12 2011. © Kate Allatt

When the Allatt family met Eamonn and Ruth on ITV's This Morning *breakfast show, May 2011.* © Kate Allatt

Overall winner – Extraordinary Woman of the Year awards, May 2011 East Midlands. © Kate Allatt

Anniversary 'comeback' tandem bike ride, Derwent Reservoir, Sheffield, May 2011. © Kate Allatt *(Family and friends had completed the same bike ride route in 2010 to raise funds for me!)*

'...Anything you can do!' Climbing, June 2011. © Kate Allatt

Nordic Walking in the Peak District, June 2011. © Kate Allatt

Glammed up in my posh pink dress! Presenting at the 02 Media Awards, July 2011. © Kate Allatt

An 'angel' sings. Anita sings on our Special Day when Mark and I renew our wedding vows at Christ Church, Dore, Sheffield, May 2011. © MCPHOTOGRAPHY

The happy couple with India and Alison muscling into shot!
Wedding Renewal May 2011 in Christ Church Dore.
© MCPHOTOGRAPHY

Our family members with 'imposter' aka Alison, Maid of
Honour, May 2011. © Kate Allatt

Woody waits in anticipation to 'mummy and daddy' walking down the aisle. © MCPHOTOGRAPHY

Pluto joins India, Harvey and Woody. Disney Florida, June 2011. © Kate Allatt

and instead wrote, 'REALLY SORRY, WE MISSED THE TRAIN!'

A split second after Alison sent that that text to my co-writer, she wrote,

'...ONLY JOKING! HA HA HA!'

Except the second text did not get received!

There was a half hour dip in our signal on the train, during which time my co-writer had a sense of humour failure.

It must have seemed a lot longer before she received our follow-up text saying,

'.........ONLY JOKING!'

We received a rather serious text back from my co-writer who politely hid her frustration, anger and panic. Instead of us sharing a funny, genuinely innocent joke with her, we almost gave her a heart attack at 7.45am!

Missing the much listened to national, live Jeremy Vine Radio show wasn't an option for the small independent publisher, and I was a new author with a book to promote. Missing the annual prestigious book fair didn't bear thinking about!

I am not exaggerating when I say that we laughed all the way to St Pancras! Consequently, my ribs really hurt, as I struggled to walk to the station loo! (I almost had to reinstate my 'Tena Lady' accessories!)

Arriving at St Pancras, everything seemed so big; it was my first real venture outside of Dore and Sheffield since late January 2010. There was a long walk to the waiting taxi where my unfazed co-writer was waiting for us in the vehicle with an extremely chirpy, East End cabbie.

I became unusually quiet and nervous. After all I would be speaking live on air to millions of people. What if I froze or stumbled over my words or even got the nervous giggles? I so wanted to get my book message across and raise the profile of Fighting Strokes. After all I had been through there was no turning back. I had a goal and I was striving to achieve it. Would Locked-in stroke patients be listening? I couldn't go wobbly now. Focus...focus.

Arriving at the BBC radio studios, in Great Portland Street, the nerves really kicked in!

Rehearsing the points I wanted to say over and over in my mind, the magnitude of the next half hour one-to-one interview suddenly dawned on me!

The researcher took me straight up to the 'Green Room' to try and relax and wait for our call.

The radio station was being streamed into the room as the producer came into introduce himself and went straight to Alison with his welcoming arm outstretched thinking SHE had recovered from a catastrophic stroke. He ignored me totally! It was highly comical.

That was enough to end the eventual silence from our train trip. We broke into laughter again!

My co-writer still couldn't enjoy the funny side of things and certainly wasn't amused with our blatant immaturity! But it certainly broke the ice for me.

In the studio I was greeted by Jeremy Vine and I thought, 'How tall is he in real life?' As a big fan, I had always listened to his show before and after my stroke every day from midday until 2pm and during my recovery period at home.

The interview started. I nervously name-checked everything I planned to say, although a lot I didn't intend to say too! Mr Vine was adept at extracting some really 'close-to-the-bone'stuff, but then I'm often far too open with my feelings anyway. As you can probably tell, I didn't hold back, (but then again, I never do!)

That interview, 14 months on from my stroke, still drew comments and some very positive feedback. The responses to my Facebook beatinglockedinsyndrome site were truly amazing. There were people coping with horrific illnesses, other stroke survivors, health professionals and people who had thought that their lives were tough.

The producer shook my hand afterwards and was visibly moved by my interview. I just said, 'It was how I felt, I wasn't media trained, but I spoke from my heart.'

As I left the studio for the Green Room we saw our first celeb, Duncan James with his band mates from boy band 'Blue'. He insisted on stopping me to kiss ME four times, having just heard my live interview. He was visibly moved by my journey, life and fight. He had been there to publicise their forthcoming Eurovision Song Entry, 'I Can' which seemed quite apt at the time. I felt a sense of pride that as far as the interview went, 'I had' got all my points across succinctly.

In just one hour, my interview on the Jeremy Vine show catapulted my forthcoming paperback from 3,008 in the charts to number 57 on Amazon's Future Bestsellers list and my publisher was suitably impressed. It was to be her first top 100 published book and we celebrated with a glass of champagne on her exhibition stand! (As a matter of interest, that chart position later became number nine, then eight, in 24 just hours!)

That is the power of radio. I once felt silenced and trapped and now my voice – albeit not completely back to normal – had been heard by millions of people across the airwaves. It felt quit liberating to know I had been given an opportunity to speak about my experience and people valued what I had to say. It was a good feeling and my friends revelled in my happiness.

The day was going well with plenty of interest in my book. We'd managed to grab some Paninis and water at Olympia, but then I needed the loo yet again. (A weakness from seven months of catheterisation.) On my return to the book stand, my publisher met a buyer from UK book giants WH Smith and she introduced me as the author of a 'truly remarkable' book. He, like most people, looked puzzled as to what Locked-in Syndrome really meant and what 'Running Free' was all about. So, as he shook my hand, I grasped the opportunity to deliver one of my killer lines.

'Hi, are you familiar with the author, Jean-Dominique Bauby and the film '*The Diving Bell and the Butterfly*'? Well, sadly he died...PAUSE...

'...and I didn't!'

Judging by the way his demeanour immediately softened, he knew Bauby's story, and in turn gained an insight into my very different story.

My publisher loved my one-liner, though Alison thought I could have had a gentler approach! Well, I had to tell him how it was. After all, a legacy of my stroke is that I am even more direct than I used to be. If I could use the minimum amount of words to get a message across, I would. I did not have time to pussyfoot around or acknowledge people's feelings and I often wondered if I offended people with my 'call a spade a spade' approach!

Another mad media moment was when when Mark and the kids accompanied me to share the sofa with Eamonn Holmes and his wife and co-presenter Ruth Langsford on the ITV show 'This Morning'. This had come about from the great flurry of media interest following my 'Daily Mirror' interview in November 2010.

Little did I know that then that the screened appearance of Mark and me would provide future endless nights of dinner party ribbing!

Eamonn , questioned his wife in a puzzled, unsure way about my book. He asked me questions off camera, which suggested he hadn't read it, let alone been briefed on it!

'Three, two, one.... ACTION!'

Eamonn exactly knew my story, as he introduced my book, flashing it to the camera. He was very up to speed and we consequently totally relaxed on the sofa. The earlier vagueness was a ploy of his, I'm sure. To get the guests open up and say a bit about themselves and relax.

The pre-planned script for the interview went out of the window as the interview took a whole different direction. It was fun as Eamonn joked about us being like them, 'An old married couple!'

Then I delivered the line that would provide endless 'ribbing' fodder. Eamonn said,

'So MARK, (I'd already talked a lot), what was it like for you and how did you cope?'

To which I said,

'I'll answer that! I just want to say...' the studio fell into giggles, as I hogged the limelight but it was genuinely really only because the interview was about to be wrapped up and I hadn't made all my pre-planned points I wanted to make – that's my excuse!

Harvey went up to Eamonn in the commercial break and enjoyed discussing Manchester United players, transfers and recent team results.

Four days after that legendary experience on the sofa was another media first for me.

I'd been shortlisted as *'Extraordinary Woman of the Year 2011'* The awards ceremony took place at the East Midlands Conference Centre in Nottingham. Mark, Alison, Anita, Mum, Colin (dad's brother) Carole, Ann and Kevin were there to support me.

One of the original *'Calendar Girls'*, Tricia Stewart, was a speaker. She was hysterical as she mapped out the real-life timeline of the story behind the film.

My category was 'Personal Endeavour'. I felt elated when I won the award.

I began texting my friends and updating my Facebook status, whilst the event organiser announced the Overall Winner. This was biggest award and quite an accolade to win. I genuinely never thought it would be me.

'Kate put your b***** phone down!' said Alison under her breath.

'... And the winner felt like she had been 'buried alive...'

'S*** it's me,' I realised!

I quickly stopped texting and started concentrating on the ceremony, whilst trying to look cool.

The awareness for 'young strokes' and specifically 'Locked-in Syndrome,' didn't stop at these awards as I discovered over the subsequent months.

My charity trustees plotted for our charity to take part in a new game show, *'Holding Out For A Hero'*, which highlighted the work of a 'hero' and gave a nominee, Jaqui the chance to 'win a life changing amount of money' for their chosen charity.

They plotted with the ITV acquired company, 12 Yard Productions (responsible for the worldwide hit show *'The Weakest Link'*) for months, all the time I thought we were being filmed for a documentary called, 'Choosing a charity'.

Michelle, Daniel and Sue agreed to be interviewed and I was pleased with our relatively new notoriety when in the middle of filming the documentary, Jaqui interrupted our trustee meeting to announce her apologies for arriving late. Jaqui was never late for anything.

I was in the middle of filming a piece to camera as I subtly (even though I'm told that I don't do subtle) inferred we were in the middle of filming. As Jaqui persisted in apologising to me. I was getting irritable that she was disturbing us.

After what seemed like minutes of apologising she made an announcement and I felt everyone's eyes upon me.

'Sorry Kate, I will have to stop you now, because the reason we're all here is because we all think you are pretty special and I want to do something special for you.'

I stopped in my tracks as I wept uncontrollably. I was crying because of four things.

a) I was in shock. How was this surprise kept secret from me?
b) Friends were doing something so incredible for me and my Fighting Strokes charity in terms of raising its profile on national TV and potentially boosting funds if game show winners.
c) Wow! We may be able to help Michelle Wheatley!
d) We were potentially going to able to afford an administrative assistant to help me with my bulging workload.

The show was incredibly well organised from the runners, to the researchers, to the producers and make-up artists. Both Jaqui and I were groomed to an inch of our lives and treated like celebrities and we all got to meet game show host and former rugby player Gethin Jones who was lovely. He said had found my story very moving.

The game show mainly required a lot of luck but also far more general knowledge than I possess. Jaqui, with her wide array of general knowledge was a great nominee, as she kept calm and collected under the studio lights and thought the answers through out loud.

Jaqui knew the last answer, as she did the other three of five question answers, but she unluckily chose low value monetary cards which sent us into a negative cash total and a long way then to go to beat our next rival charity team.

It all came down to the last question with Jaqui needing to select a monetary card with a value of £16,000 or more to beat the front-runners and win the game.

Then the card-reading machine broke for half an hour.

As Gethin made the announcement, we immediately knew that we had lost the game by a few thousands. Jaq picked a card with a value of £11,000.

However, we figured that the actual winners (East Hull Amateur Boxing Club – which really benefits the community and gets young 'would-be Rocky' boys and girls off the streets and gives them a sense of self worth) were more needy. (In terms of their ability to generate future funds and raise awareness).

Though we did take a £3,000 consolation prize home and we have some great memories to boot.

The media interest in me has at times been overwhelming and I have had to get up to speed on contracts, exclusives and the general way 'my story' is packaged and delivered for mass consumption.

On the plus side, I have learnt a lot about the media and myself too. The fact I like to be in control of my story. (Hence this self-published book!) Will I forever be labelled Kate Allatt the Stroke Survivor? Is it all of my sum parts or just part of who I am? How much of the pre-stroke Kate Allatt lives on? I certainly have the same drive and ambition to get on with things.

Yet, will I achieve everything I want to from now on? Will people get fed up with hearing about my story? For the charity's sake, I truly hope not. I anticipate there will be challenges and issues, which will continually be addressed by Fighting Strokes in order to help other stroke survivors worldwide.

Who knows, maybe even Sylvester Stallone (I've written letters to his agent) will officially support my Fighting strokes charity. (Perhaps you, reader, can help make this happen!)

I have a sense of pride about the awards I have won to date. There is no doubt that the media can get the aims of my Fighting Strokes charity to a great many people. There was a time when I thought my identity was totally wrapped up in being a stroke survivor –, but as months pass and the situation seems less intense, I realise I am far more than the label bestowed upon me.

Yes, I had a stroke and I am helping others with my charity. But I am also a mum, a wife, a friend and an individual in my own right. At times, it feels as if these very important aspects of my life have become somewhat overshadowed.

I need to focus on other things too and others have to be comfortable in the shift of how they may see me. I have grown in confidence and I am less needy. That takes some adapting for others too. I have always felt comfortable in the role of the one being needed- that is why I felt so worthless when I was Locked-in. What could I offer? I could not even communicate my fears so they lay latent and unexplored. If you cannot communicate how you feel, others don't know how you feel.

Now I can, if I want to, tell people exactly how I felt at the time, how I feel now, and how I may feel in the future. Not all stroke victims/survivors/patients will share the same thoughts but it is important their voices, fears and hopes are heard.

That is how the media can play an important role.

For five whole months I was silenced by my stroke. For a businesswoman who, by nature, is outgoing and talkative, I felt like a once bouncy and entertaining Jack-in-the-Box toy that had been stuffed back in the box with the lid locked shut. Inside my head I was summoning all my energy to scream, 'I AM in here! Let me out!' More importantly, spring out and cheer everyone up.

I have never been a wallflower type and I often mused that my marketing degree had never prepared me for not being able to talk. It was totally frustrating – and I couldn't even let out a few choice words! I could not get my anger out. An array of expletives – stretched slowly in my mind as I inwardly saw each elongated letter squash into the next – used to swirl around inside my head; black tangled eels feeding off every small particle of pain and despair that entered my active brain.

As my voice has gradually returned I have taken a new path in a different world (which strangely feels very similar and also far removed) from the one I left, as I was stretchered onto an ambulance on a cold February evening.

With the help of four singing lessons and sheer determination on my part, I realise the round of interviews, radio and TV appearances meant I HAD to communicate again. Even though I worried about my voice not being properly understood at the time.

What I did not initially expect were the great moments of mirth and merriment, the amazing makeovers and being made to feel I am a person who matters. After all, that is my aim for all stroke survivors. Their voices can be heard in equal measure – whether through Facebook, Twitter and social networking.

Or, just like me, they may be inspired to write their own unique story.

For that, I am truly grateful.

Chapter 9 –
Mum's Dead!

Quite unexpectedly, after such great progress, I hit a very desperate low. I'd even experienced real suicidal feelings which alarmed me. I still wasn't taking anti-depressants, as I believed I did not need them. After all, I had my life back and everything to be happy about hadn't I? Also, I wasn't 'in-therapy' for my changed emotional state.

I loved my family SO much, yet I suffered with enormous guilt too because I had thought of doing such a dreadfully selfish thing – even though I wanted my inner emotional pain to end. I was no longer a fun loving mum who was able to discipline effectively. I felt like a pathetic shell of a human being. My family life was unravelling before me as my very public, professional life was soaring to new heights. How can someone 'love' their new purpose in life but also really want out of life? I was doubly confused about these feelings.

I hated showing any kind of weakness to Mark's parents, in fact anyone for that matter. I was exposed, naked, stripped back, vulnerable and utterly lonely in my new stroke survivor head. You could say that I was almost as lonely as I was in ICU. Depressing.

But things got worse.

The day after we returned from our long haul flight from Florida, India woke me from a very deep sleep at around 7am (I had eventually fallen asleep only two hours earlier.)

I immediately and quite ridiculously quickly, rose from my 'pit' and flew downstairs to the bathroom. (Our bedroom is in the attic, up two flights of stairs.) I momentarily leaned on the sink as I felt quite queasy, light-headed and had that old familiar piercing stomach-ache. Still, I then turned the shower on and waited for the water to heat up.

I would soon feel better. Then I felt decidedly worse. My head felt dizzy.

I thought:

'I'm going, I'm going to...'

Just as the world froze I did have enough foresight to shout, 'HAAARVEY, WOOODY, INDIAAA....' Who were all downstairs watching TV.

Then nothing. I'd collapsed.

Meanwhile, India called Mark at work – an hour's drive away. All he heard was from Harvey and India were the chilling words:

'Mum's dead!'

Mark, working on the principle that there was an issue with me, on average about once a month, panicked. He tried to call back and get any information but the kids were busy dialling 999 and Alison. For 20 minutes or so, as he bundled himself into his car, he couldn't find out anything. Was I really dead? Terrible thoughts raced through his mind as he recalled the 'sick-stomach-churning-fear' of the day I had my stroke.

India had the common sense to call Alison, who in the meantime dashed round to the house where she saw Harvey in tatters, screaming, crying and completely devastated.

Woody didn't really understand what was happening and India just took control. She was reacting like an adult would, in a very Sergeant Major, organised military way. (I'm actually really very proud of her).

My lovely next-door neighbour, also called Kate, was cradling me in my birthday suit when I awoke.

I'll never forget my first words to her.

'C-A-N Y-O-U H-E-A-R M-E? D-O Y-O-U U-N-D-E-R-S-T-A-N-D M-E'

She responded with,

'Y-E-S I C-A-N'

'Phew! For a moment, I thought I had another stroke!' I told myself, not realising everyone had shared the same scary thought.

Embarrassingly, I again was driven off in an ambulance to hospital, (I'm certain I'm now known as the village 'sick' person) and I brazenly tried to flog my first book to the paramedics! In my heart, I'd felt it had been a fainting episode. However, this time I was relieved that the NHS medics weren't taking any chances with me. So I happily let them help me.

Mark visited me in A&E before I got transferred in another ambulance to the city's specialist stroke unit.

The whole day was spent undergoing endless tests and stroke assessments. Although my abiding memory was, 'OK enough now, let me go home.'

Apart from wanting to escape the doctors' seemingly over cautiousness, Alison had uncharacteristically annoyed one by sternly telling her that surely she had 'far more needy patients to see to on the ward.'

It was that day that I had to remind a doctor, who was examining my reflexes, that 'laughing uncontrollably' was a stroke side effect and not us messing around. In truth, Alison and I were really joking around but I must have made the doctor feel bad. I must have been better, we were being SO mischievous!

Eight months earlier I had fainted in my local curry house, Almas, whilst celebrating my earlier hospital release and underwent an endoscopy. I wasn't given a full anaesthetic then, and it was pretty unpleasant as doctors manhandled the food into my stomach. Yet again, Mark, Alison and my mum were there to visit me after my over-nighter in hospital.

As I 'came round' on the floor, my first thoughts were all about my new crisp, white Karen Millen shirt.
My first words were, 'I've been bloody sick on my new shirt!'

Alison knew it was only a faint but Mark turned white with worry. I do put him through hell. Things just seem to happen to me.

Two months later, YES! would be in yet another A&E unit in Majorca with an over large piece of beef stuck in my gullet stretchered off on a huge yacht. Alison joked at the time that I was going to extraordinary lengths to check out the world's A&E facilities!

Food stuck in my oesophagus is a regular occurrence for me. For example, the chunk of turkey that was removed by endoscopy with no anaesthetic and the choking-on-a-meatball incident the day the Queen visited Sheffield to officially open a motor-neurone diseases centre.

What have I personally learnt from these incidents?

ALWAYS CHEW YOUR FOOD & DON'T EAT STEAK.

GET UP OUT OF BED SLOWLY, AS I HAVE VERY LOW BLOOD PRESSURE.

GIVE MARK A BREAK.

DON'T HAVE FUN WITH DOCTORS.

MUM IS NOT DEAD; SHE'S BACK...ALIVE AND KICKING!

Chapter 10 –
The Cook, the Beef, Hols Life
(and Death) Cover!

Take my advice. *Always* take out holiday insurance cover. This story reveals why!

It was a beautiful, balmy night in Majorca as we sipped cocktails and relaxed in a beach bar near Palma. The sun looked like a bright blood orange globe and the evening sky was streaked with iridescent hues of pink and gold. The sensational sunset was one of the best we had seen. It was one of those nights out with friends when time just whizzes by because you are having so much fun.

As we chatted and enjoyed our drinks, we soon realised the sun was now nestling on the horizon. It felt as if a radiant yet tired Mother Nature was turning in for the night. Still buzzing with holiday excitement, we had no such plans to call it a day. We were still in our bikinis, tee shirts, shorts and flip-flops, make-up free with unkempt hair and wrapped in our hotel bath towels and sarongs. We were intent on chilling out, laughing and having fun.

Through the darkness we heard a friendly, well-spoken American voice.

'Would you ladies like me to take your photo?'

'Yes please,' we replied in unison.

We all agreed it would be great to have a photograph of us girls together which captured us at our most relaxed and happy.

As we passed the camera to the rather toned and fit looking man, we gave our biggest smiles and relished in the moment as the flash went off. I felt so normal again, back with the girls.

As he handed the camera back, the American, invited himself to our table to chat.

'Lovely shot ladies, a good one for your holiday album.'

We agreed and we got chatting about the beautiful sunset and the fact we were on a special girls' holiday. His friend, also American, soon pulled up a chair and joined in the conversation at our table. He was also very fit looking with muscles that suggested he was into working out. He sported an array of tattoos. He told us he was a chef.

That's when us girls started to have a bit of fun. We said he did not look like a chef. He did not look like a stereotypical food-loving cook – not the kind we were used to seeing back in the UK. He did not have an ounce of fat on his body.

'No, sorry, you are definitely not a chef. We don't believe you. You have too many muscles,' said Alison cheekily (at which point I thought to ask her if she had ever seen Steven Seagal in 'Under Siege' who utters the words 'I also cook' – but thought better of it).

After 20 minutes of our teasing, he smiled warmly and said, 'I'll darn well prove to you ladies I am a proper chef by cooking a meal for you tonight. You'll see!'

At that point we hadn't eaten, so the offer was very timely, so the four of us accepted his generous offer. We were dressed for the beach, but thought, 'what the hell?' We were being offered a lovely meal, we were hungry and Alison had subtly checked with the barman that these two regular customers were decent and honourable. The report back was that these were respectable men and we got the impression they were not only well-liked by the beach bar staff but were not the usual 'tourist' customer to grace these shores. We were to be proved right when we realized our meal was going to be rather special indeed.

The first American said, 'I hope you ladies can get on our rig boat out there.'

We gazed in the direction he was pointing out to sea.

So, our meal was going to be aboard a boat. (The use of the word 'boat' seemed to create a slight smile on the first man who had introduced himself.)

'Er, yes, our, er boat is out there, if that is OK with you ladies?,' he asked.

We all looked at each other and laughed. This holiday was turning out to be full of surprises and soon we were taking a trip on the barman's own rig boat to the chef's bigger and more robust rig boat.

As the girls steadied me on my feet, I climbed in and we sat huddled in the back with the wind blowing our hair all over the place as we zoomed around the bay to Palma and saw our 'restaurant' come into view.

The large white vessel was a vision. A luxury yacht of the sort owned by the uber-rich. We learnt that our rig man (the first man) was actually the captain and his muscly tattooed friend was his personal chef who cooked for him and his 11-strong crew.

And we would be dining at the captain's table!

As we climbed aboard the yacht, we could not believe our eyes.

'OMG!'

'OMG!'

'OMG' or in Alison's only words that night,

'F***'

The super yacht seemed totally extravagant. It had been recently upgraded with trendy, minimalistic furniture and room accessories. There were four spiral staircases and even a lift and Jacuzzi! What's more, we discovered that the boat was only worth a mere £45 million and cost £3 million a year to maintain it!

'F***,

F***,

F***'.

Alison uncharacteristically repeated use of this swear word (thankfully I have not developed Corprolalia – involuntary swearing after a stroke – some people confuse it with Tourettes... but to leave out my swearing would not be a truthful or accurate account of the night's events.)

As we were taken on a grand tour of all four floors, kitchen, bar, captains helm, Jacuzzi, guest rooms, crew quarters, sun deck and other polishing and gleaming rooms which looked as if they had been transported from the pages of Millionaire's Yacht Monthly – if such a title exists.

That was when Alison in her excitement gave me my bloody, black eye. She yanked me towards her so suddenly in her utter excitement that she failed to see the powered sliding door, which shut in front of me. I comically bounced off it with a bruise Tyson would have been proud of delivering!

The champagne and nibbles were enjoyed for the hour and a half it took the chef to rustle up our meal, during which time Jaqui and Alison sampled the Jacuzzi's' water temperature.

We were totally buzzing and perplexed as to how this night had changed from a quiet end-of-the-day cocktail in a rustic beach hut near Palma to a luxury yacht with a restaurant area where everywhere you looked screamed opulence and wealth. We were hardly 'dressed for dinner' in our beach garb but our companions treated us with warmth and kindness and seemed genuinely interested in what we had to say and did not look too bored when we got out snaps of the kids and husbands we had left at home.

Dining at the captain's table and chatting to him about his yacht journeys was fascinating, and the chef sat down to enjoy the fruits of his labour and prove to us he really was a gourmet in the galley.

As the six of us settled down to a midnight feast of huge, thick steaks and Dauphinoise potatoes (I don't use the word 'shovel' lightly as normally ate at 6pm and was bloody starving), I shoveled in one, two, three mouthfuls of the deliciously succulent beefsteak. The best I had tasted. Then, in my mind, I said to myself:

'Oh s*** it's stuck!'

I sat in lonely, mild panic at the table as the others chatted, whilst secretly hoping that the piece of beef would pass through my gullet into my stomach. Next, I tried to coax it down with *Coca-Cola*, which just made me vomit... in colourful cocktail colours...all over the pristine 'so-posh-you-don't-really-want-to-use-them'cream napkins. I could not have felt more embarrassed. I'd been sick at sea on a stationary yacht!

Anita noticed my boisterousness had stopped and mouthed to me from across the table,

'Are you alright?'

With all my effort, I managed to get one word out in deliberate, unmistakable way.

'No!'

Alison looked worried. Anita and Jaqui looked across at me and froze.

'Do you want to go to hospital?'

'Yes!' I grunted.

By now I could see everyone staring at me with worried faces.

'Oh crikey,' she said, whilst retrieving her mobile phone to call the Spanish emergency services.

Within 20 minutes, the Spanish paramedics were boarding the moored-up boat in Palma.

At that point, the process of establishing that I did indeed have travel insurance began.

I didn't have records of documents so Alison dialled Mark at midnight in Sheffield.

'Kate is absolutely fine, DO NOT worry... but can I have your travel insurance details?'

Understandably he was half asleep and immediately concerned.

'Why?' he asked as he tried not to worry that his wife was a long way away and in trouble.

She explained that a large piece of beefsteak was stuck in my gullet, but not my windpipe.

Mark stayed calm and gave Alison the necessary details and told her to look after me. He wondered what on earth it was about me that seemed to attract 'events.'

As Alison finished the call, she tried to stay focused.

Yes we had both had quite a bit to drink, but that was even a humorous affair as I lay in agony, and Alison proceeded to play charades in front of the nonplussed Spanish nurses.

'S-H-E H-A-D L-O-C-K-E-D I-N'. My desperate friend mimed turning a key to unlock a door.

'And she's recently had a S-T-R-O-K-E.'

Alison slowly stroked her arm and the nurses stared at her as if she was a madwoman.

If she were a contestant on the old popular TV series *Give Us A Clue*, she would have given mime expert Lionel Blair a run for his money. Although her strategy of adding

English words with the manic arm movements was somewhat lost in translation.

With my impromptu hospital stay, I had managed to spend €3216 on three nights away.

Was I glad I'd taken out holiday travel insurance!

All I remember of that night was Alison, until 2am fretting by my bedside in an annoying way, while I tried to distract myself from the pain of having a large piece of beef stuck in my throat.

In her unusual guttural way she drunkenly repeated over and over,

'Kate, Jaqui's going to f-ing kill me because I lost her phone in the ambulance!'

I'm thinking for a while quietly how I wish she was quiet, then all of a sudden I erupted in a similarly, unfeminine way,

'Shut the f*** up!'

Alison looked shocked. I had never in all our years of friendship, spoken to her that way. I wasn't being a very supportive friend that night I know, but I needed to stop feeling the pain by going to sleep. The night's events been quite overwhelming and I needed rest. The others could continue with their fun.

At 2am, after checking my following operation plans the next day with the Spanish nurses, she left my bedside. Surprisingly she managed to find her way back to the others on the yacht. Knowing was in safe hands, they continued to dance the night away until 7am. I hoped the sight and smell of my vomit had not put everyone off the rest of the meal.

There was no point in curtailing my friends' fun. They could tell me all about it in the morning. Indeed they did, how the crew members were the perfect gentlemen and were genuinely concerned about me. I must have given the chef quite a shock but by the time I was stretchered away he had convinced me of his culinary credentials.

More importantly, he knew I knew he was definitely a chef...although things had not gone entirely to plan. I am certain he has never had other diners end up in hospital!

The yacht certainly surpassed the 'Champagne O' Clock' adventure of two years ago. Too bad the wind had been taken out of my sails, so to speak, just as the party got started.

Perhaps somewhere in an exotic location, the tattooed chef is cooking his steak (or working on his six-pack) and recalling the time his specially prepared food, delicious as it was, nearly killed an Englishwoman.

Belated compliments all round!

Chapter 11 –
Wedding Bells Again!

In spring 2011, with a feeling of new beginnings in the air, Mark and I renewed our marriage vows in a packed Christ Church, Dore. It felt extra special to be back in the church on May 15th where Mark and I were originally married in 1998 – 13 years to the day. I could never have imagined how my life would have changed. I am very blessed to have three wonderful children and a loving husband who has always been my best friend as well as my soul mate.

I was the one who, back in July 2010, actually suggested renewing our marriage vows. At the time, I was in a wheelchair and could only manage a two-yard shuffle when I tried to walk. I was in my hospital room when I asked Mark to 're-marry me, please,' in a very matter-of-fact unromantic way. I wanted him to know I was trying to rebuild our deep connection which I felt had been somewhat shattered by my stroke.

Looking back, it must have seemed a strange thing for me to say as Mark quickly replied 'Why would we do that? I'm still married to you aren't I? We don't need to remarry to show our love.'

A week later, he had changed his mind. (Isn't that a thing men *always* do?)

'Anyway', he said, 'I've been thinking about your marriage proposal and our wedding renewal. You know I would love to remarry you and see you walk down the aisle. Yes please. Bring on your and our next goal!'

Holding my bouquet of fragrant white lilies and roses on that chilly May day, I was thankful that my sense of smell had not disappeared forever. It was a shock when it did go AWOL following my stroke. Perhaps not being able to smell 'eau de hospital' in the early days was a blessing in disguise as I had my fair share of antiseptic smells to contend with later – and other whiffy moments that are best kept private!

119

I recall the first time I smelt the scent of daffodils again. Alison brought a bunch into hospital and 'threw' them in a vase. I was shocked on three counts.

1) My best friend could not flower arrange to save her life. How did I not know this?
2) I could smell again. The daffodils smelt heavenly and I was thrilled I would not be forever derived of a sense I had perhaps taken for granted.
3) Spring was indeed springing without me.

Back then, as leaves grew on trees, flower buds sprang into life and Peak District lambs gambolled on hills near my home – I was totally oblivious to the world moving on as normal without me. Alison's daffodils had signified that time was racing ahead without involving me. I felt like a dormant bulb waiting to push upwards and onwards and burst into life and experience sunshine again. It is not until you lose anything that you realise how much it is valued.

I could have lost my life and by 'life' I don't just mean me as a living human breathing person – or indeed my 'active' life as opposed to a 'trapped, Locked-in existence.'

I refer to my everyday married life with layer upon layer of shared memories, in-jokes, private moments, comfort, security, surprises, challenges, recollections of the kids mispronounced words and off-beat expressions and a whole lot more. The various facets of togetherness shared by a couple and the routines and patterns of married life that nurture the soul and glue you together. A stroke can affect all that is dear to you, so you have to keep your wits about you and stay one step ahead.

The legacy of Feb 7th 2010 is that the wife Mark married has been replaced with a different person but he still loves me unconditionally. For a long time, I was a patient, not a wife. Our renewal of our wedding vows was also a celebration of Mark and I actually staying together against the post stroke marriage statistics. (Apparently, strokes and other conditions lead to an increased incidence of marital break ups, as do other health injuries and afflictions.)

My worst nightmare would to be stuck in a hospice with round-the-clock care and I would be a wife and mother on the sidelines of my family's everyday life. Perhaps these fears drove me to 'pop the question' again, who knows? Deep in my heart, I knew that I'd made the right decision when I married him 13 years ago.

In the run up to the 'event' we have been overwhelmed with the support from family and friends including many new ones had been made since we moved to Dore.

Getting ready for the 'wedding' was, just like the last time, full of funny moments, as indeed they should be. Then was added excitement about 'the dress.'

I had ordered my cream and black dress from 'Coast' in Debenhams which I knew fitted my new physique. (Think post-stroke ever-so-slight 'muffin top') due to my body not running 70 miles a week for some time...though I was back exercising.

Shortly after I was discharged from hospital, Alison came round to help me into it, as I wanted to see how it fitted. We were in the downstairs playroom and my stepdad Dave was washing up in the adjoining kitchen.

Alison gently lifted the dress from the hanger and assured me that putting it on would be easy peasy.

'Sit down and we'll put your feet through the bottom, then we'll slip it up.'

I sat on my sofa and hooked my feet inside the dress. We managed to pull it up around my waist, and then zip the dress up. It was a pencil shape, so it was very narrow at the knees, which restricted my ability to balance. I went to stand up and suddenly toppled over rigidly upright as if I was a tree being felled.

I collapsed onto Alison and we deteriorated into uncontrolled giggles, as Dave wondered what all the commotion was about. I couldn't help imagining this happening in the church with me toppling onto Mark or even into the vicar's arms! Fortunately, after a few more attempts at walking in a more ladylike and less zombie-like way I quickly got used to the way I could move around in it with ease (I had been in my comfy tracksuits for some time), but warned Alison to stay near on the Big Day in case I needed catching!

Eight months later, my old photographer friend was snapping away on our special day at the back of the traditional church, which held such poignant memories for Mark and me. With each click of the shutter, it was difficult not to reminisce about my life up to that point.

Each special memory entered my mind in a freeze-frame moment. The birth of my children, the various family holidays, my time with friends. And of course the fact I had married a fantastic man who proved he would love and support me through the darkest of days. I could so easily have not been here today. I fought back my emotions of utter relief, happiness and realised just how much I had accomplished.

Anita began to sing *Ave Maria* as I entered the church with Mark (who looked as amazing as he did on our original wedding day). He seemed outwardly emotional as he normally keeps a lot of emotion in but I think we both felt so very overwhelmed by the occasion.

Even though I had instructed Alison not to let me look up, I did just that. As Anita's beautiful gentle voice emanated from the front of the church, it seemed as if her voice was being carried on a piece of ethereal invisible chiffon swirling down and enveloping us with warmth and love. Quite simply, we were touched by her gesture and the fact she had been taking singing lessons and this was her first public 'performance.'

The small church was full of my dearest friends and relatives and but seeing them all in one place was quite something to take in. There were people who had been in this same church 13 years ago, and new friends we had met since we moved to Dore. They were all here for us! There were many faces I had not seen for 18 months and as I locked eyes with some of them and saw deep emotion reflected back to me, I started crying again, quite noisily and Mark put his arms around me and gave me a gentle squeeze. I could tell he was just as emotional as me, as were our children.

I thought back to our original wedding day. How could Mark and I have ever known we would be back here with three special children?

Anita's beautiful singing now had an unscheduled backing track of my sniffles and blubbering. I must have sounded like *'Donkey'* from *'Shrek'*. My tears just seemed to pour out but I knew people would understand my noisy sobs were due to my utter happiness, elation, relief and remarkable sense of pride that I was not in a wheelchair and I was making an attempt to be the 'old' pre-stroke Kate. Besides, many of those in church were visibly crying too!

Walking behind me was Harvey, as were India, Woody and Alison (my Maid of Honour). Mark was protective towards me tenderly wrapping his arm around me. It seemed that he had no interest in suppressing the sheer pride he felt to be accompanying his wife, walking down the aisle.

The vicar welcomed us all to what was actually an incredibly, emotionally charged event.

We all stood up for *Praise My Soul The King of Heaven*, followed by a bible reading from Alison's husband, Chris. Next up were our kids who had each prepared a special reading for the special day.

India read her own words.

'Hello, as you know I am the eldest in our family. Last year was the hardest ever, when you think of the worst things in life then times it by 10 times, that is how hard it was. I am so happy and proud of my Mum's progress. Also I have to thank my Dad, as he has been amazing, He's gone through the pain himself. When I think back to everything he had to do to keep the house under control, it must have been awful like doing the following: Cooking, working, going to and from the hospital, and looking after us and doing house jobs, he must have had a lot on his mind! I am happy that everything is back to normal. I wouldn't have had the extra boost if it weren't for my amazing friends, so I would like to thank them. I am so

happy to be here this time to celebrate my mum and dad's' Big Day. Thank you for listening.'

She passed the microphone to Harvey.

'Hello, as you all know my Mum has been through a lot recently and being the middle child, in the family has been hard for me. Last year it was so hard for me, India, Woody and Dad because my Mum had a really bad stroke. I am so happy that my Mum has made an amazing recovery. My Dad has been so good at doing jobs like, cooking, cleaning and everything else Dads' do. I would like to say thank you to my friends and family. Thanks for listening and see you at the party!'

Harvey then passed the microphone to our youngest, our son Woody.

'Hello, I am the youngest in our family. Last year the thing I missed the most were my Mum's hugs! I also have to thank my Dad for looking after me while Mummy's been gone, as well as my grandparents. I am looking forward to the big, bouncy slide. Thanks for listening!'

There were more tears amongst the well wishers. As the vicar made his address, he welcomed us up for our vows and I was first with the microphone as I turned to face Mark.

'Mark, my husband, best mate and real hero. Thirteen years ago we made a pledge before God, family and friends, to be committed to one another in this very church, on this very day. You have more than passed the ultimate test and you honoured your original vows. We still don't always agree, but our relationship is far deeper, more connected. I hope that in another ten years, it won't have been like the murder life sentence you often joke. You have made my family life complete and given me the security I craved, during our good times and our recent, extremely tough times.

Thank you for sharing the nurturing of India, Harvey and Woody, I think you'll agree that their resilience has been remarkable. I have always loved you and I always will.'

Mark tried to choke back his tears when I handed him the microphone.

'Kate, you are my wife, mother to our three wonderful children and most importantly my best friend. Thirteen years ago to the day we were married in this same church. The vows we made on that special occasion have become the most important words that I have ever said, especially given the challenges of the last fifteen months. Today, in the presence of our friends and family, I am delighted and honoured to renew my commitment to you. To love and support you and remain with you for the rest of our lives.'

Later on, after more singing from Anita, Jaqui and her husband James were up at the altar for their bidding prayers. It had been an emotionally charged ceremony James spoke eloquently with his Sergeant Major type voice.

'Heavenly Father, we pray for Mark and Kate today as they both reflect and look ahead. Lead them as they move on into the next chapter of life. Help them as they guide and support India, Harvey and Woody as they continue to grow. May their home be a place of fun and joy, security and peace. And may they continue to be aware of your help and encouragement. We pray in the name of Jesus Christ the Lord. Amen.

May we also all give thanks to Mark's new garden shed! Amen!'

The deeply emotional congregation immediately fell about laughing at his bizarre, out of place comments, which was led by hysterical laughter from Mark. The atmosphere was immediately lightened as we left the church and headed for a thank you party at a local rugby club. In case you are wondering about the garden shed-it was a place of escapism for Mark when he wanted to clear his head and every man should be blessed with one!

Shortly after arriving at the rugby club reception marquee, we felt on cloud nine despite the chilly weather. Mark assembled the crowd of family, children, and friends. A large gathering, which included the vicar, Mark's work colleagues, local friends and some of my pals from university days. With one visiting from her new home abroad. Our youngest children's primary school head teacher and the vicar were also present for the only wedding speech of the day.

Mark began with his huge long thank you list for the local community; people who had rallied so much for our family. All the people who had left the family homemade dishes at the door and all of those who offered practical help were mentioned. He then mentioned the way our family had been touched by the general way the community of Dore had been there in our time of need. He obviously thanked grandparents and Anita, Alison and especially Alison. In his words, she went above and beyond the call of duty as a friend.

He is also extremely dangerous with a microphone, as he likes to talk. He soon got into his stride and I couldn't shut him up! I worried that our guests would freeze to death in the unheated marquee as Mark talked on...and... on...and on! By now I feared the ice-cold guests might just want to get on with the buffet meal and retreat to the rugby club bar for drinks and enjoy the specially ordered chocolate fountain.

Mark continued,

'One evening while Kate was in hospital, my friends didn't quite know what to say to me, but I was in a mid conversation with one a bloke about...'

I thought to myself, 'Oh No, no no! He's going to tell them THAT story in front of all these kids, my parents and the vicar!'

I froze and avoided eye contact with everyone as I heard Mark continue.

'...*not having time to even have a....*'

Our family and friends gasped at the totally inappropriateness of what was coming, as they'd all read my first book. Then he paused, whilst thinking to himself, 'I'm in a corner, what do I do?' and obviously had a revelation when he found more 'appropriate' words.

'...*man tug!*'

To which another friend, who hadn't heard my story innocently asked if '*he could do anything to help?*'

Fortunately the crowd were polite enough to laugh, (again) though there were some embarrassed parents' faces and the vicar's too I hear! Fortunately the joke went over the children's heads and in any case the majority were outside on the bouncy castle.

A week after our wonderful celebration, we headed to Cornwall – honeymoon with kids! Our southwest trip had been billed as a spectacular return to a favourite holiday location and 'normality.' Just like the old times, we thought.

Except it wasn't.

Once the holiday was underway, I quickly realised I was very disabled. I couldn't do any of the things I used to take for granted. Morning runs around the headland near Harlyn Sands, rock pool fishing, swimming with my kids (because I had a habit of nose-diving), or even putting on a full length, keep–the-cold-out wetsuit from 'Big Dave's' surf shop. All of these activities were complete no-no's. I felt a complete failure.

I found controlling my footing on the sand almost impossible and grew angry at Mark's daily disappearances to the beach pub without me. Little did I know that he was secretly plotting my surprise ITV appearance on the new programme, '*Holding Out For A Hero*', and had enlisted the help of Alison and her husband Chris to sort out the necessary preparations with the TV executives.

It would be honest to say that I hated Cornwall in May 2011 as I begrudgingly spent a week behind a windbreak to contemplate the crapness of my new 'disabled' life.

We only had two weeks before we left for a holiday of a lifetime in *Disneyland*, Florida. Perhaps, as I grew stronger each day, things would be different.

My old and first best mate from school, Donna, had done a sterling job fixing up all our travel arrangements. The car, a detached house with swimming pool and even a whole family upgrade on our *Virgin* trans Atlantic flight. The kids had been officially granted permission to be taken out of school to go abroad during the last weeks of term time and that alone thrilled them.

Harvey was so excited with his personal games and TV console. I took the precautions of wearing my special T.E.D. stockings, but allowed myself a few celebratory glasses of fizz. It took three films and a half- hour nap before we arrived in our united states of euphoria!

The kids were SO giddy. Us parents loved to see their excitement. They deserved this break. We all did. But would we all feel free and brave on this special trip to America?

After changing our hire car for one with a bigger boot for a foldable wheelchair, we were off.

Arriving at our quarters we were excited about our safe gated community and our own private swimming pool. It might have been late in the day but the kids couldn't wait to get their kit off!

We planned to visit Universal Studios the next day.

It proved to be by far the best day as we were fast tracked on every ride from Harry Potter to Spider Man, as I was 'disabled' in my wheelchair.

I loved breaking rules (and did I heck?). Even though I was a registered Blue Badge holder, I loved cocking my head to one side whilst claiming 'I'm disabled' to get preferential treatment. We did the park rides in super quick time. It was brilliant! I decided that there weren't many perks to being 'needy' but I'd just found a great one. After all I was not going to be in a wheelchair forever. When I was lying in a hospital bed I felt useless. What fun could I provide?

Back then, in my Locked-in state, I was incapable of making my kids laugh. Here, I could make sure they had the best holiday ever. Strange as it may sound, I now had the power to make things happen. Maybe I was caught up in the excitement of the *Disneyland* resort but I felt like a magical fairy helping my children's wishes come true.

I loved watching the kids get wetter by the minute on the log fumes. It was so rewarding to see India laugh uncontrollably as she is a theme park fanatic. Harvey discovered, much to his surprise, he actually liked the log flumes, but he shares my fear of heights.

I engineered things so I would often get pushed to the front of the queue, where no fast track was available, for these 'scary height' rides. Then, as my family waited next in turn for the ride, I'd pretend to wimp out as I explained I'd changed my mind as 'I've had a stroke and I'm sure this would be too jerky to go on.'

The Disney employees, possibly scared of potential litigation, continually let my family push to the front of the queues, while I sat and waited. Suddenly, in my kids' eyes, I was the coolest mum in the world. As they returned, high on adrenalin, their smiles (not to mention Mark's Cheshire Cat grin) said it all. Mum had sprinkled a bit of her own magical fairy dust again!

I do remember a kerfuffle by the pool when the kids spotted a highly poisonous snake in the water; I quickly realised it was dead, not sunbathing. It spooked the kids somewhat as our pool was surrounded by an abundance of cleverly designed netting to keep predators out yet let the sunshine in. Harvey and Woody proudly displayed their trophy in fishing net! Another holiday story for the childhood memory bank. I'd rather have the children build up memories of 'remember the time there was that orange dead snake in our pool?' or 'remember when mum helped us go on all the best rides?' instead of 'Remember when mum couldn't join in the fun as she was stuck in that wheelchair?'

Slowly, we were all readjusting but we were a long way off from becoming *The Waltons*. (And show me a family that is!) Our American dream holiday was fantastic, don't get me wrong but it served to show me the state of all our relationships following my time in hospital. It was quite upsetting.

I witnessed, really for the first time, the state of all our relations after my incarceration.

There was a new emotional distance between Mark and me. Ditto – between the kids and us which broke my heart. I thought how I'd worked so hard for ten years to raise our kids to be kind, friends and considerate, when in eight months those relations and respect had been irretrievably damaged. I enjoyed them, enjoying their holiday, however it was a huge wake-up call in many ways. We were all out of control. It was as if my stroke had been a huge bowling ball that had been hurled at us and we did not know which way to lean as we fell down.

The kids fought continuously and there were many fracas played out in front of the American public. I felt we were pathetic, weak parents. The children? Emotionally mixed-up and unsettled.

On the plane home, I was again upgraded due to my disabilities and my family were assigned seats in 'squaddie class'. For the first time in two weeks it was peaceful again and I loved every minute of it.

As I drifted off to sleep, I realised my kids had enjoyed a great holiday but changes had to be made. I would NOT let my stroke impact on my family this way. I had the power to change things.

The kids had one more week of school, then we all had the six week summer holidays to look forward to. I would be with them every day. Oh what joy.

I could sort things out and make up for lost time. Forget about fun-time 'Mom.' I had to get family life back on an even keel. Mum was well and truly back!

Chapter 12–
Tantrums & Tiaras

Just surviving the summer holidays with three strong-minded, and often feral kids was no mean feat! I now truly understood why their behaviour was so challenging for both sets of grandparents the previous year – when my stroke turned their lives upside down. Alison, with her boundless, positive encouragement, used to repeat a mantra.

'Kate, you *are* getting there.'

One day I may believe it! On the first day of September term, the school gates were open and the quiet 'village' of Dore filled with excitable children. India, Harvey and Woody were stocked up with packed lunches and new school bags, pencil cases, paper notebooks and pens. All togged up in their new school uniforms, they were keen to catch up with their friends' news and there was a tangible 'Back To School' mixture of excitement and uncertainty in the air.

Honestly, I truly breathed a huge sigh of relief as I dropped them off. I was not one of those parents who seemed quite mournful at the end of the school holidays. Yes, we had enjoyed our time together – tricky though it was at times – but for me, the new autumn term brought peace and quiet.

Don't get me wrong. My kids are individually adorable, kind, loving and incredibly mature for their young years, having been through a very difficult time. However, the three of them together was like some sort of World Wrestling Federation event with me failing to referee! I felt emotionally knocked-out by their frequent outbursts.

Woody is loving but his tantrums are at the high end of the Richter scale in terms of loudness and general magnitude. They can erupt daily anywhere in Sheffield at any time.

Harvey is a complex, sensitive, loud and 'gobby' middle child, who needs to be exercised (or tired out to use up his energy), as you would a dog (and I mean that in the nicest way!) twice a day. India is very nurturing; she has great qualities, which will make her a wonderful mum one day. But she has some alien hormones rampaging through her body. When she erupts I don't stand a chance with her motor mouth, as she morphs into a real-life Vicky Pollard from Little Britain (as explained in chapter 4). All this is perhaps entirely 'normal' pre-teenage behaviour, yet I myself wasn't 'normal and at times felt I couldn't cope with challenging behaviour I would have previously dealt with firmly and fairly.

My friends suggested a total break from routine to recharge my batteries with a three-day holiday in Majorca. The Spanish island was a destination that held happy memories for all of us. (These memories helped me stay positive when I was Locked-in.) Could we 'recreate' those moments and capture some end of summer sun? A chill-out change of scenery certainly seemed as good as a rest. It was a wonderful idea.

The first night was a quiet affair. The second night saw me stretchered to the hospital in Palma. However, as I slept like a baby on the hospital trolley (In my swimwear), an unusual spat was unfolding in a nightclub in Magaluf!

Let's just say that alcohol, a shortage of 'evening out spending money' and no recollection of the name of the hotel in which we were staying – combined with tiredness and panic – were all catalysts for the exchange of a few cross and uncharacteristic words between Alison and Anita that morning. Tiredness played a major part in the fall-out. They *had* been out clubbing (after my yacht incident) until 7am!

Just to recap what I had done in just three days. I had... 'you really couldn't make it up!'...

Sunbathed and met funnyman 'Mr. Guest' and his friends and played many practical jokes around the pool.
Joined in a game of pool volleyball.

Drank cocktails in a beach bar as the sunset before being invited onto a £45 million super yacht by the captain and his chef.

Received a black eye from Alison (by accident) when she unwittingly pulled me onto a sliding door when showing me around the luxury yacht.

Had to be taken by paramedics to Clinica Juanedo hospital (where charade-playing Alison lost Jaqui's phone) following the stuck beef incident on the yacht –prompting an immediate panic back home in Sheffield.

Felt quite out of it following an endoscopy to remove chunk of beef that I thought was going to be the end of me.

*Personally negotiated a premature hospital discharge and spent a fortune in medical bills (Thank f*** for insurance cover) but felt shaken by the incident.*

A lot of unscheduled 'fun', which I am certain you won't see in any holiday brochure, I'm sure you'll agree.

When I flopped onto my sun lounger that same day at 12.20pm, I was suffering with a post-operative razor sore throat but felt overwhelmingly relieved that I had survived yet another ordeal. Lazing in the sun, all of these incidents went few whizzing around my head. I winced as my cold drink travelled down my throat and concluded:

*'B***** hell, it's needy Kate all over again.'*

'What must Mark have thought, at home in Sheffield, when Alison called him in a less than sober way?'

*'Why can't I just b***** well fit in, instead of being the centre of attention all the time?'*

Alison broke my solemnity by suggesting that I just couldn't keep away from the world's A&E facilities. She was excellent at reading my mood and was trying to raise my spirits but I kept thinking, 'Why do these things happen to *me*?'

I told myself I would take things carefully. I proceeded to enjoy soft drinks and ice cream for the rest of the day and night!

Unsurprisingly, I was quite tired by the evening when we had all gone out for an Italian meal and cocktails. I was determined not to be a party-pooper but felt strangely deflated.

'Heellloo girls!'

Mr. Guest and his friends who were at the same restaurant and appeared to be in high spirits – their normal exuberant selves, had spotted us. As they joined us for dinner on a big table, I ate alone. I started tucking in to my meal before anyone else had even ordered. I was ravenous, my blood sugar level was low and I feared I would faint if I left eating too late. Anita was holding court showing family pictures on her phone, and Alison and Jaqui were chatting to Mr. Guest and doubled up with laughter as he told yet another witty joke.

Everywhere I looked, everyone seemed to be having fun. I just couldn't get into the night. To cap it all, one of Mr. Guests' mates accidentally threw his red wine all over my new beige linen trousers. After everything I'd been through that day, it was the straw that broke the camel's back! I felt all eyes upon me and I was extremely angry but kept my feelings to myself. I could have got emotional there and then, but I fought back my tears on this occasion. Nobody knew how I was feeling inside – quite overwhelmed by the unexpected holiday drama and the fact I felt out of my comfort zone.

It seemed surreal. I'd had a major stroke, now I was 'recovered' and on holiday. One of the girls again. But was it really as simple as that? It wasn't. I had changed, and I knew it. But did anyone else understand? If I had tried to explain that night, it would have been wrong. There were expectations that I should be good old fun Kate – out of hospital and back with her friends – but I honestly felt like an imposter.

At midnight, I wanted the evening to end, so Alison offered to walk me back to our room and promised she would return within half an hour.

On hearing her promise, I metaphorically did a Rocky punch in the air – through sheer relief...and victory too.

Why? Because I hadn't shown any personal weakness in asking her to stay to babysit me. This was HER decision. But oh how I NEEDED her to return. I felt completely out of my depth.

I tried to sleep with nervous butterflies in my tummy caused by my high levels of anxiety, insecurity and fear. Somehow, I must have drifted off to sleep.

BANG! CRASH! GIGGLE.GIGGLE. SH.... UUSH!

My body 'jumped' as the loud noises awoke me suddenly.

I looked at my watch. It was 4am as the three girls crashed into the room, waking me up.

'What time do you call this?' I asked in an irritated voice before drifting back to sleep. I felt furious and confused with the strength of my emotions. Why was I feeling like this on holiday?

I woke early the next morning, still fizzing with fury inside and feeling really quite unusually emotional.

At breakfast, I couldn't make eye contact with anyone, not even Alison. This was probably the first and only time Alison had REALLY upset me. In her typical style, Alison quietly took me on one side by the pool to ask what was wrong with me. I didn't hold back. I was concerned that she knew that my outburst wasn't some sort of jealousy because I wasn't out partying too until 4am with them. This outpouring from the usually 'considered- risk' taking Kate, was actually all my thoughts spilling out about how I was totally SHIT SCARED of dying alone!

That night and morning, I'd had time to dwell on what could have happened to me alone in my hotel room.

For example, I knew doctors didn't give general anaesthetics in the UK for an endoscopic procedure. I knew that because I'd already had an endoscopy in the UK. I also knew that a general anaesthetic, back home, would be considered an unnecessary operating risk.

The truth is, that in a former life, I would have been the first to say 'yes' to dancing in Magaluf and in reality been the last one home! Did I wish I wasn't so delicate? Of course. Could I do anything about it? No. In effect, I felt trapped again – this time by my new and very real vulnerability.

The reason I was so angry and emotional was because I knew I'd pushed for my early hospital discharge, to hit the sun loungers for me and my long suffering friends, at the potential cost (in my mind) to my own immediate health and well-being. I had developed a very real fear of hospitals and operations, rather like some people have a phobia of flying or lifts. I also felt weak, shaken and sore, as a result of my procedure. Was I emotional as a result of everything that had happened? Of course. I was an absolute wreck.

I had actually WANTED 'babysitting' and protecting, but didn't want to be seen as asking for yet more help from my good friends – not even Alison.

'Kate really IS disabled,' that was my initial thought but there was a deeper fear I had to acknowledge. One I had never openly talked about.

I was scared of dying in a lonely hotel room in Spain. I was genuinely terrified of hospitals and operations of any kind because I knew of post-operative complications with anaesthetics. It is accurate to say that the operation was far more complex than was expected and the bill cost €3216 more than estimated.

Yes, quite a funny tale now and I enjoy telling it, but at the time it felt as if I was in real danger. When you are in another country a long way from home, you crave your familiar surroundings. When I was pushing for independence and new adventures I didn't realise I would feel like this. Insecure, unsafe and frightened of the unknown.

Sure, I should have not been too proud to ask for help, and I do recognise that my friends are so keen not to patronise me with practical assistance. I understand that they 'back-off' out of respect. I had to have help in hospital, but asking for it now when I was 'out and about' seemed like a backward step. But wouldn't the benefit of hindsight been great? Before I'd even packed my holiday bags?

I collapsed on the sun lounger as my uncontrollable tears ran down my face for all to see. Kate the Brave was an emotional wreck. It had a taken a holiday abroad for me to acknowledge I was not unbreakable. At that moment in time I felt fragile and was afraid I'd never feel strong again.

The moral of this story, as I see it.

I must never forget, how patient and selfless my friends are and were. (Some would say long suffering!)

Always know where you are staying on holiday.

Remember to take extra money other than the kitty pot, for unexpected emergencies.

Always stick together.

Acknowledge that my friends do recognize that I am so much better than I was, but they should be aware that I am still extremely delicate both physically and emotionally.

Remember that my need and requests for help should not be seen as a sign of weakness. Friends and family are not mind readers!

The air was totally cleared and we all enjoyed our last two hours of sunshine.

I had travelled to the Mediterranean on a mission to have fun and feel 'normal' and I returned with great memories, a healthy tan and a newfound respect for my friends and myself. I have never wanted to feel a 'victim' as I know I am a survivor against the odds. But even survivors have to realize when to let their defences down and to ask for help.

Post stroke recovery is a journey of discovery and learning about how to adapt to a new life – with old friends and expectations.

Perhaps, like a bird flying the nest, I had been seen as someone who took everything in her stride. The truth is that those friends and supporters who so desperately want you to be the 'old' person you were, also learn that you are not and to some extent never will be. I don't want to be treated like a delicate princess but I do want friends to know I am still on a learning curve in relation to moving forward. I know I am making excellent progress but there may be times when I have to reveal my hidden vulnerability.

Yes, It was a case of feeling I was Gonna Fly Now! And my short break had given me a taste of freedom, which I relished. Yet, I knew that the tantrums served a purpose and good has come out of it. I had stretched myself to the limit physically and emotionally and something was bound to snap.

Fortunately, the emotional holiday 'baggage' from that outburst has been left abroad. I hope that others who have suffered strokes can learn from my experience and not be afraid to express what they feel, for fear of being thought of as needy or 'disabled.' A stroke does disable you physically and emotionally but it is how you cope in the future, which will impact on your well being on all levels.

Those around you need to know how you feel and what you need. You may feel as if your life map has been crumpled up, straightened out and needs to be re-written all over again – not just for you, but also for those around you.

When I dissolved into tears on the lounger, It was as if all my pent up anxieties and frustrations which had also been Locked-in with me, had been set free. I returned from holiday feeling quite revived and having learnt a great deal about myself. Placing myself in a new environment has made me see that my friends and family mean the world to me...and what's a few tantrums among friends?

I have said this before and I need to believe it. I am not superhuman. Considering all I had been through, it would probably have been quite unusual if I had not shed a tear or two on my first proper sunshine break abroad with friends since my stroke.

I am no longer Locked-in but I definitely don't hold the key to all of life's little setbacks. I am a normal person who has been on an extraordinary journey.

But remember this. It's not just children who have holiday hissy fits.

You just have to get over them and move on.

Chapter 13 –
Fighting Strokes

FIGHTING STROKES
Young & Locked-in Syndrome

Empower & inspire those affected by all brainstem strokes and Locked-In Syndrome to promote better recovery, especially in the young.

What does Fighting Strokes do?

We will actually help any 'Locked-in' brainstem stroke sufferer. We specialise in supporting those affected by this condition, both emotionally and physically. We believe that the best chance of recovery will be influenced by patients' willingness to 'fight' their debilitating symptoms. Motivation and access to early great therapy, are more likely to enable the patient to recover in our opinion.

The registered charity is wholly concerned with the advancement of health of stroke patients and the saving of lives in particular but not limited to the following:

1. To raise awareness of stroke recovery.
2. To inform carers and health professionals working with survivors.
3. To provide support for family and friends.
4. To provide practical patient support.

Aims and Objects. What do we offer?

Information
Support
Advice
Visits
Campaigns
Fighting Strokes wristbands
Promotional material

Fighting Strokes came about when I met my amazing friend Sue Sandars (herself a stroke survivor, though not Locked-in) and we both realised we had a zest for life and 'bloody-mindedness' in spades which could be put to good use.

We are really happy to work with all support groups including The Stroke Association, Different Strokes, Speakeasy, The Speech and Language Association and Strokes Suck – to name a few.

Anyone with an interest in stroke recovery is welcome to contact Fighting Strokes and we believe sharing information is useful for all! I just must add that this message goes out to Mr. Sylvester Stallone too! It would be more than I could ever dream of if you agreed to become a patron of this charity! Please get in touch!

I thought up the idea for my Rocky type hero punching the air victoriously (centre of the eye) because – just in case this point has passed you by – it was the fictional fighting champ Rocky Balboa from my all-time favourite action-hero 1976 film who inspired me to fight back to recovery and help others.

Both Sue and I have been real fighters but in Sue's case, she is quite different from me.

Why?

She did not imagine she was a tough and muscly American underdog turned boxing champ reincarnated in the lifeless, inert body and actively alert mind of an English female hospital patient 30 plus years after his cinematic

Knock Out victory. You really couldn't make it up, could you?

Following chats with Sue and lots of other stroke survivors, it soon became blindedly obvious it was only me who did the weird stuff!

On a more serious note, everyone will fight back a different way and with different goals and milestones (and may even use different visualization techniques) but that doesn't matter. The most important thing is to keep fighting!

We do understand the turmoil stroke survivors face during insight initial stages of diagnosis as well as post recovery.

Our own personal experiences have, we are proud to say, already helped others.

Did you know that only 5% of the stroke care budget is spent after leaving the patient has left hospital and that strokes are currently the third biggest killer behind cancer and heart disease? (And tipped to hold second place soon).

The most profoundly shocking news for us is that the recent NHS cuts have had a massive impact on stroke care services.

When I initially founded Fighting Strokes, I envisaged raising great sums of money to pay for stroke patients' rehabilitation. The vital speech and physiotherapy stroke patients require after they are discharged from NHS facilities to specialist neurorehabilitation centres around the UK. However my vision, I soon realized, was not going to progress as planned.

What I did not know back then, is that Local Authority (or other trust funding) is MATCHED to whatever the charity has fundraised. Perhaps I was slow on the uptake, but I soon realised I'd given myself a totally unworkable task. I was acting all alone in the role of charity administrator and the workload was immense. I always set my standards high but even I knew I had been over-ambitious.

With specialist rehabilitation costing upwards of £35,000 for three months for just one patient, my vision was not humanly possible. Fighting Strokes would, I soon discovered, not be able to actually help many people each year – if any!

I had placed tremendous pressure on myself, especially in these belt-tightening recessionary times. However, on a more positive note, there was a realisation that my charity could make a difference to other stroke survivors' lives.

I was fortunate to receive a lot of feedback following my hospital, hospice and home visits and various Skype conversations with people both in the UK and around the world. One thing became perfectly clear and to be honest I felt quite chuffed when I realised I had totally underestimated just how my own knowledge and personal stroke experience could provide vital help to others.

The resounding message coming through loud and clear was that about people wanted a connection with others who are going through a similar stroke experience. Patients and their loved ones wanted support, visits, advice and as much information as possible.

There is a real need for real practical advice, knowledge, reassurance and a powerful voice to influence the medical world. People tell me I give them living, breathing hope. My personal story and my visits and chats show them I am not a one-off medical 'blip'.

We could change medical expectations for the way brainstem stroke patients are treated worldwide. After all, there are so many other success stories out there and Fighting Strokes has given me a positive focus to give back to others.

My new friend Mark Ellis collapsed at work in August 2010 following a brainstem stroke, which affected his speech and left him unable to walk unaided. It was soon after the birth of his baby daughter Lola-Rose.

He was just 23 years old and doctors did not think he would survive. Mark's wife Amy saw me interviewed on ITV (Yorkshire) Calendar TV news when he was initially in hospital and contacted me on Facebook.

Incredibly, as Lola Rose is learning to talk, she is actually helping her dad learn how to speak again now he is back home. I have met Mark, Amy and Lola-Rose and they are such a close-knit family of three despite their shared ordeal.

I could see for myself the poignant and strong connection between father and daughter and how strong Amy has been. When I was invited back to Calendar TV, along with India and Woody, I felt privileged to be talking about the Ellis family and knew exactly what they were going through.

I said that Mark has the right attitude, so much fight, as has Amy. To have them on board supporting Fighting Strokes is amazing, You have to believe you can do it and be positive in the face of all the negativeness out there, to say 'No I don't want this for my life I want something else.' I'm no medical expert but I believe the power of the brain has something to answer for. It is really touching that Mark's daughter is now learning to speak at the same time as he is learning to talk again. It was my youngest son Woody (mentioned earlier in my book) who encouraged me to say his name in hospital – my first word since my stroke. He had faith I could do it!

I was thrilled to receive messages from Christine Waddell who has been Locked-in for 15 years and is just a bit older than me. I am proud to say I phoned Newcastle University, near her home location, to suggest they use Christine's case as a research dissertation project. Christine cannot afford expensive rehab costs so this is delightful news. Watch this space!

Christine Waddell

Hi Kate, hope all is well, I just can't thank you enough for Thursday, I am just feeling so positive now. We found a private neuro physio like you said and its a snip at £64 an hour ha-ha at that price ill get him every day not. No, I don't care how much it is as long as he can help me, speak soon. btw, I have sent you a friend request. Bye for now. xx

Kate Allatt

Got a result at Newcastle University. They are dead keen x

Christine Waddell

Excuse the French, but bloody hell; I think Carol misheard the price for the physio. The price list came this morning and its going to cost £500 for the 1st visit and about half that per hour after that. Great news about Newcastle University though. xx

Christine Waddell

Hi Kate, can I just ask you something? Before you learnt to talk again, could you make the shapes with your lips as if to mouth the words? I'm sorry if it sounds nosey, just I can't do it. x

Kate Allatt

No. My mouth and tongue did not move at all.

Christine Waddell

Kate, I can't believe it, but I have just moved my thumb!!! xx

Kate Allatt

That's fantastic!!!! Three weeks should know something from Newcastle University. Xx

Here's my most recent email from Christine Waddell. I received it on 28th March 2012 and made me so happy given Christine has been locked-in for 15 years.

Hi Kate, I've just received the wristbands and they are brilliant. Thank you so much, I really appreciate it. Anyway, I've just had the best ever news. I had my neuro physio assessment on Monday, which sounded very positive indeed and she has just phoned to say that she wants to bring a Botox specialist to meet me. She thinks that maybe she can get some more movement than the neuro physio can. Plus, I have to take her report to my GP and try to get the PCT to fund it. Any persuasive ideas? Thanks Christine xx

Andrew Bell and Heidi Davies are other people who have received support from Fighting Strokes. Here is Andrew's story in his own words.

By Fighting Strokes on Monday, 19 September 2011 at 18:35

At the age of 30 I thought I was fitter/healthier than most of my friends; I really enjoyed cycling and squash, and I have never smoked. One morning on my cycle to work, I didn't reach work. That day in A&E was probably the scariest in my life so far, slowly losing control of my limbs and speech. The next day I couldn't talk at all, nor eat; I was bed bound. That was the start of what has transpired to be quite a journey.

One Monday morning during my cycle to work, having felt that I was getting a migraine, I got off my bike and sat on a low wall at the side of the road. I used to get migraines quite frequently so this wasn't particularly unusual. They difference started when I slipped off the wall and couldn't get back up. A passerby stopped and he flagged down some passing police who called an ambulance. I could talk and recall being fairly compos-mentis to begin with in A&E. It was clearly not obvious to anyone what was wrong; I felt that I was physically weak, both the doctors and I seemed to think it was a particularly bad migraine. When I tried to pull down the zip on my cycle jersey I couldn't co-ordinate my action, which was when it actually became quite scary to me.

I had MRI and CT scans but it wasn't until the evening that the doctors saw something of note to them on one of the scans. I now know it was an Ischemic stroke in my Basilar artery. I recall that nobody used the 'stroke' word, but I was moved through the hospital (most of the lights were out as most people were asleep) into a ward that had 'Acute Stroke Unit' over the door.

The next day I couldn't sit up in bed (let alone leave my bed) couldn't talk, couldn't eat. I was also labile, which manifested in crying; any emotion resulted in crying, I used a lot of tissues!

I communicated with thumb up, down and sideways. I was fed through a tube in my nose that went directly into my stomach. I went to the toilet and was washed, in my bed. During one of my first bed baths the nurses were discussing my sexuality while washing me. I couldn't talk, nor move much; I was still there and able to listen and will probably remember that forever. Throughout my experience there have been great people and the not so great.

I was in the stroke ward for what like felt like forever. Being one of only 2 young patients, I was 30 the other was 54 it could have easily felt like a very lonely place. Everything was at the bed, eat, sleep, read... only physio was an opportunity to leave those small confines. Many of the specialist staff (phyisios, speech therapists and nutritionists) were the closer to my age than any of the patients. It was good to have this contact; some of them have since told me that they could personally relate to me than the older patients and really wanted to make a difference.

I was massively grateful for the support of family and friends. I was never short of visitors in the evenings. Days, especially initially, would feel extremely long and I very much looked forward to when visitors started arriving after work. I understand that my church even organised a rota so that visits would be well spread, with not too many at one time and nearly daily someone visiting.

Having never really been in hospital previously it was an unknown situation to be in and know how to deal with. I found that my faith was a massive strength to turn to; my church friends were able to support me in trusting that Christ was in control. I found reading biographies of Hudson Taylor and those who worked with the China

Inland Mission deeply encouraging, and helped maintain and strengthen my trust and faith in Christ.

After 11 weeks I was moved to a re-hab unit, which was a really different experience to my weeks in an acute ward. We had wheelchairs that weren't taken away all of the time and got to go for a 'wheel' as/when we liked, it was actually encouraged. The nurses didn't do everything for you; you had to try and would only get help if you really needed it. We had the opportunity for quiet by our beds or be in the communal room when we liked (outside of pre-programmed speech therapy, OT, physio). We ate meals together in the communal room outside of our ward, away from our beds; this really encouraged social interaction and friendships to form.

I enjoyed being with people my own age again. They hadn't all had strokes, but all had some neurological reason for being there, those closest to my age mostly had GBS (Guillain-Barré syndrome). A group of 4 of us got on particularly well and started wheeling out to a local pub in the evening, and probably all felt a race to be first to stand, first to walk, first to be able to pick their nose...

After a few weeks there I started having supervised weekends at home before being permanently 'released'. My first weekend away was 150 miles on the train (in a wheelchair) to my parents' house and a friend's wedding. The weekend was very liberating after weeks with hardly any outdoor experience (and included injecting myself with my daily blood thinners in the car park at the wedding).

I left re-hab after 9 weeks and returned to my flat, back to living by myself. I was able to walk about inside without any aids, but used a wheelchair when outdoors. I continued with private speech therapy, occupational therapy and physio.

Unable to easily get out and do things that I used to do I started cooking and baking, I found this cathartic. It was also good exercise for my hand that I still hadn't much control of and standing. When I did go out I found that buses and taxis were more accessible with a chair than I had appreciated. It was also very noticeable that the travel getting to, and back from, places that was perhaps more tiring than actually being there.

Not long after I left hospital I proposed to a lady who was just amazing while I was ill. We are now married. We have been away on honeymoon and weekends away together; I have also been able to do DIY to accommodate her things in my flat; it may take me longer than before the stroke but still satisfying to make things myself.

I was very grateful for the visitors who made the effort to visit me at home. Just because I was at home rather than in a hospital is didn't mean I didn't appreciate, want or perhaps even need visitors. Although I was out of hospital things were very different to before I went in.

After 2 months of being at home I started back at work for a few hours three days a week. Whilst in hospital and initially my work was very supportive, it was certainly one less thing to be concerned about. I have more recently been finding it more difficult to increase hours and fully integrate back into the office life. I think there is a mixture of not understanding what I am now capable of, and also not wanting to do anything that may have any negative impact on my recovery.

Getting back to work has been a balancing act that constantly needs monitoring. The need for time off for hospital appointments and physio, management of fatigue, adjusting my role and responsibilities as I regain the ability to undertake tasks all affect what work I am given to do and how well I can do it.

Being at work has meant that I have had to be out of the house and able to organise myself. I think it has been quite beneficial in that respect. Also being with different people and interacting with colleagues, clients, consultants and suppliers have really been socially encouraging and motivational. It has reinforced that I don't need to be worried about my speech, it is good enough to communicate, and the liability is manageable, particularly in my work environment.

By the end of private support, a year and a half later I was walking outside with a stick.

My main hobby before the stroke was cycling. I am unable to ride a bicycle; due to balance, but have recently bought a trike. It is great to be able to have some independence of travel, I can cycle places far easier than walk to them. I have found that feelings of frustration and anger have massively reduced since having the trike. My wife certainly feels that I have adjusted to whom I now am.

It transpires that my stroke was probably caused as a result of a bicycle accident some years earlier, though it isn't certain. I have since had angioplasty to repair the neck damage where a clot may have formed and wash out into my brain, which hasn't been 100% successful; I have regular cranial angiograms to monitor the situation. I am still on blood-thinning tablets and tablets to help with the liability.

I am now married. I now walk with a stick. I work part-time 5 days a week. I am a better baker and I ride a trike.

Life hasn't ended, it has changed, but I can't really grumble.

Heidi Davies also tells her story.

I was 32 and was expecting my second son, during my first son's pregnancy 5 days after the birth I suffered with high blood pressure, so my second pregnancy I made the midwifes etc know this. Then 5 days after his birth on the 21st June 2009, I woke up with the worst headache I've ever had. My husband took me back to the maternity unit, which is 30 mins by car as local Drs etc were at lunch (another story), only to arrive for the fire alarm to be going and they wouldn't let anyone in, when they finally let us in (which felt like ages but probably wasn't). My blood pressure etc was taken which was rising, I then started to be sick, they then tried to take blood but it wasn't happening, my husband always says he then knew something was wrong.

I was rushed into the emergency room, were I vaguely remember one of nurses talking to me, it was my husband who said to them, she's had a stroke, as my face had dropped, after this I don't remember anything. I was moved to ITU in my local hospital, my husband was told nothing more they could do for me. Luckily for me a consultant said he would call London. He then came back to say the Royal Free Hospital in Hampstead said they would take me. When I arrived I was taken for a scan and then had surgery, I had a bleed out, I don't know all the technical stuff as I can never seem to remember it all (my husband is the expert).

I then spent a week at the Royal Free, and then was transferred back to my local hospital for a week, where I was given physio and OT sessions. It was a mission just getting out of bed into the wheelchair to go for Physio. I remember them sitting me on the physio bench, to see what my balance was like well all I'll say is it was non-existent; I kept falling to the left. When I was medically stable I was transferred to our local Rehabilitation unit in Canterbury, Kent, where the physios and OT's were fantastic. Teaching me to do everyday tasks again, which I took for granted before. Simple things like dressing myself, which used to be quick but then, took hours well that's how long it felt. I stayed there for 3 months; I could have stayed longer but being stubborn and the emotions of knowing what I was missing with my new baby. I asked to go home, the Therapists & Physios were great and got me tackling steps etc, as I lived in a house, although we were in the process of selling to move to a bungalow to make my life easier. I left the Rehab Unit on 1st October 2009, so was home to help with the move (supervised from the chair!). We moved to the bungalow, 2 weeks before Christmas and I started to get some independence. Mastered the art of changing nappies one handed, it can be done. I then fell in the kitchen in March 2010 and broke my hip (never rains but it pours!). Just thought I'd make it that bit harder for myself, ha ha!!

Everyday whilst I was in hospital my husband would bring my sons to see, which really motivated me and made me want to progress, in the early days my eldest would come in the morning and then my husband would come back again in the evening with our newborn son.

Later both boys came together, which eased the trips for my husband.

I returned to work in Aug 2010 on a phased return back to my role as an Administrative Specialist, which I left when I went on maternity leave. Work were very good and my OH contact was always on the end of a phone, they ensured everything was set up, providing voice activated software as I do a lot of computer work, and provided a work station at home for home working. I set myself a goal in hospital that I'd take/walk my oldest son to school on his first day. It was one of those things you say that sounds good, never thought I would. So on the 6th September 2011 I achieved it. I was the nervous one than my son; you would have thought it was my first day.

I'm lucky that both my husband and me are from big families, so I was never short of visitors. I want to thank my husband for always being there for me and knowing that I needed to see my children everyday (getting a 3 yr old and newborn out the door, I know was a task in itself). For always pushing me and supporting me and still does, I couldn't do it without him.

Two years on my mobility is better, I walk short distances with a stick and you learn to make the best of what you have. I've finally come to terms with the fact that I won't ever get the full use of my left arm back.

As I say I'm still me but things are just different, so you just have to adapt.

Beth Ladbroke wrote to me with some positive comments about 'Running Free.'

Dear Kate
I have just finished reading your book and was totally blown away, it seriously is the most emotive book I have ever read and can only thank you for increasing awareness and the amazing path to recovery. I am a nurse and used to work in Newcastle in neuro rehab and nursed a few patients who were locked in and your book had made me step back and review my approach to people unable to verbalise not only due to strokes but for

other medical conditions as well. I really sincerely wish you and your family all the health and happiness in the world – much love and thank you again for sharing your intimacy in your road to recovery xx

Faith, Hope and Charity

Let me tell you about some of the reactions I get when I tell people about Fighting Strokes, how it came about and my 'miraculous' recovery. A great many people think I can offer a spiritual analysis on my recovery. When 'miracles' happen, people want answers. They want to speak about religious faith. People have different faiths, beliefs and coping strategies.

I was recently asked this question, as people are curious about my beliefs.

Amy Ellis: 'Gosh Kate, how do you have so much faith?'

My reply: *'I don't personally. I'm actually a lapsed Catholic. (I lapsed pre-stroke, not because of it) However, I do think I have a huge chip on my shoulder. I'm also very anti-establishment and bloody-minded! I choose to think any small flicker of activity, visible to the eye or not, then 'game-on' – there is stuff to work with and therapists should use all their skills to develop those signs, promote patient positivity and hope. If sadly, there hasn't been any consistent voluntary activity, then I will fight hard to improve the quality of life and the survivor's communication and social environment.'*

When I visited Andy Davies at his hospital bedside in Birmingham on Tuesday 17th January 2012, I was made to feel like a long-lost friend. Andy, his wife Emma and his incredibly warm and giving parents Trevor and Barbara, had invited me. Andy was admitted to hospital on Tuesday November 1st 2011 following a stroke, which left him Locked-in. His stroke was virtually in the same place as mine had been, the right pons of the basilar artery. Unsurprisingly, his family was pleased to hear about my recovery.

In Andy's case, the early signs are so good and like me, I think his age and general fitness is a bonus. (He is in his early 30s. He has movement in his right thumb (just like I did!) increased his vocabulary to two syllable words and is generally in good spirits, always laughing!

I felt totally uplifted to return home to Sheffield and receive this message from Barbara.

'Thanks so much for today. Andy really enjoyed meeting you. You are a real inspiration to all of us all. Love Barbara'

Barbara and her husband Trevor, also write a weekly diary for their son. It is circulated to all of Andy's family, friends and local churchgoers. Barbara's entry on Saturday 20th January 2012 reads:

'Dear Friends,

Briefly here is the latest update from Emma (Andy's wife) on Andy's blog.

Thursday, January 19, 2012
Visit from Kate Allatt.

Kate Allatt, who had the original prognosis of locked in syndrome following a brainstem stroke in February 2010, came to visit Andy on Tuesday. Kate fully came out of locked in syndrome and has since written a book and appeared on TV to tell her story. She has founded the charity: 'Fighting Strokes' and was able to put us in touch with another man in Perth, Pete Coghlan, and a guy from Chesterfield, Mark, who also had Locked-in syndrome but have made an exceptional recovery. Check out Pete walking out of rehab on YouTube; type in Pete Coghlan and visualise what it will be like when Andy walks out of rehab!!!!

Kate's visit was a very special time for Andy and gave him fresh hope. She was amazed at Andy's progress, particularly his eating and drinking, as she was nil-by-mouth for the first seven months. Kate drove from Sheffield to Birmingham and this is testimony to what an exceptional recovery she has made. Kate was inspired

*by Andy and subsequently asked if she could include his
story in her next book – Gonna Fly Now!*

*Please pray that Andy gets funding from the PCT to go
to Hunters Moor rehab.*

*Kate has been a great support to us since the early
days of Andy's stroke. Reading her first book 'Running
Free' was so helpful to us in understanding some of what
Andy was going through and how we could help. We were
then able to talk to her by phone and be encouraged by
her email messages.*

*Please pray for Kate in her work and travels for www.
fightingstrokes.org and helping stroke victims and their
families across the world.*

*For us all our assurance continues to come from the
Word of God and the love, prayers and support of all of
you.*

*'Even youths grow weary and young men stumble
and fall, but those who hope in the Lord will renew their
strength. They will soar on wings like eagles, they will
run and not grow weary, they will walk and not be faint'
(Isaiah 40:30-31)*

*'But for you who revere my name the sun of
righteousness will rise with healing in its wings.*

*And you will go out and leap like calves released from
the stall.' (Malachi 4:2)*

God bless you all keep you safe and give you peace.'

Such a *lovely* email, and I respect the fact their personal
faith gives them hope and comfort. We are all on our own
journeys with different beliefs but one thing unites every
single one of us. We all *believe* in recovery and that to
me is the most important thing. The belief in the human
spirit and the way it can overcome the most unimaginably
challenging hurdles.

Barbara's email gives me a real buzz, as I feel so
appreciated. I am so proud that Fighting Strokes is really
helping her family. It gives me the strength I need to
continue supporting, advising and visiting other patients. I
have to admit, I feel quite sad in many ways that I was not

visited by anyone who had once been Locked-in and who had fought back despite a bleak prognosis.

Andy seemed genuinely pleased I was there and it was quite an emotional moment when it was time for me to drive back to Sheffield. There were a lot of hugs. I could see how much Andy, his parents and Emma had benefited from my visit and it was very much a two-way process.

I felt quite rejuvenated when I reached the car park and quite emotional too as memories of my hospital incarceration flooded into my mind. I fought back tears as I felt for my car keys to unlock the car door. As I sat behind the wheel and turned the key in the ignition to drive back to my life in Sheffield, I realised just how special the visit had been and shed a few tears.

Oh how I would have loved to have received comforting words, a warm hug and reassurance from a 'former' Locked-in stroke survivor. Or indeed, how my family would have benefited from such a visit. We felt totally alone. I did not know there *were* Locked-in survivors walking and talking again. Back then; meeting one would have seemed as likely as meeting a space alien.

As I went to bed that night, I pondered a bit, as you often do! I realised that someone, somewhere in the world, at that very moment in time, was waking up in a hospital bed, Locked-in and alone. Had they ever met another Locked-in survivor? I truly hope that Fighting Strokes will, in time, connect survivors and patients and provide a real sense of togetherness, friendship and stroke-pal connections!

I had only read Jean-Dominique Bauby's *'The Diving Bell and the Butterfly'* – not a happy ending and not a happy book to read when you are stuck in hospital with an over-active mind. I hope my two books will be read in hospitals and be available for ALL stroke patients and their visitors.

This may sound bizarre, as I am not that religious but I like to think they would have been my 'bibles' and offered me comfort when I felt depressed and suicidal.

So, the answer readers may want to know. Have I intrinsically changed my beliefs since my stroke? No, I have not had a religious experience after all that has happened to me, however I believe in the power of positive thinking and the strength and support of family and friends – both old and new! And, yes I totally respect the views and beliefs of others. I certainly believe life is for living and we don't know what is round the corner.

To a certain extent, I am spiritual in that I recognise the sheer determination of the human spirit and the shared warmth and support offered by so many people every day of their lives. I have seen how people have the ability to support each other through times of despair. In the confusing aftermath of a stroke, it is so easy to feel as if you are stuck in limbo and life is not worth living. I want Fighting Strokes to show people *every* moment counts. Every single day is important. It sounds a cliché but it is TRUE!

It may have upset close family and friends to read me write that I wanted to die in the very early days following my stroke. Those days were undoubtedly the most difficult and painful times I have ever known.

But believe me, I am so thankful that I did not die. It may sound like a cliché, but life is far too precious as are the many people I would have left behind, living on without me. Back then, I felt worthless. What could I offer? I now know how my stroke experience has enabled me to offer a lot more than I could have ever imagined possible.

I cannot help but empathise with others who are still Locked-in with no movement whatsoever, like my dear friend Michelle Wheatley or 'Chelle', as she likes to be known.

Their days are quite different to mine, as they have not got the same opportunities I have. But, and this is the really moving part, they are so totally aware their life is so very different from their 'former' one.

Locked-in for three and a half years with no movement whatsoever, Chelle is a 27-year-old young mum-of-two who is as positive, mischievous and spunky as me. She suffered a massive stroke as she was bathing her four-year-old daughter Holly in August 2008.

It is so easy for society to forget about people like her, where the system has let her down time and time again. It makes me SO mad that Chelle gets to 'play' the social quiz, which is a way to lessen the loneliness and NOT physical therapy, and only receives BASIC rehabilitation care. I thought how she was still so funny, bright and still the same person inside, so I had an idea to help her escape her institutionalized Locked-in life.

Alison and I took her on a Christmas shopping trip at Manchester's Trafford Centre in November 2011. Because of the round-the-clock care Chelle requires, her nurses and mum Linda accompanied us.

We were to meet outside posh store Selfridges. Prior to Chelle's arrival we did a recce of the space between the beauty counters to see where her large wheelchair would fit. Chanel had the most floor area and the assistant was most helpful as she listened to our plans and insisted we returned with Chelle, if she wanted to experience a bit of pampering. I couldn't bear to see my reflections in glass, let alone mirrors, so we were prepared for a knock back from Chelle and wondered if she would dismiss our girlie adventure.

We hugged Chelle and entered the shop as naturally as we could. We wanted it to be a surprise for her. We stopped at the Chanel counter and told Chelle we wanted her to feel pampered. Understandably, she did not want face products or treatments because of her trach tube, but she loved the Chanel perfume and body moisturizer. I hoped she felt extra special, because we felt so privileged to be there and provide some fun. By the time we had left, the helpful, friendly lady at Chanel had laden Chelle's wheelchair with numerous free samples.

Next on the agenda, as chosen by Chelle, was serious spending! BIG TIME!

You remember that scene in Pretty Woman with Richard Gere and Julia Roberts in a posh Beverly Hills store? Well, when Chelle was positioned correctly in her chair she just had to gaze at her next purchase, which was chosen and then paid for by her mum who was guardian of her daughter's pin number and card. In half an hour that girl had spent two-months' worth of her social care budget!

Unfortunately Chelle gets to 'shop' twice a year, so I thought YOU GO GIRL! It was on this shopping trip that I offered to make Chelle my chief charity advisor. Her 'job' will help boost her sense of self-worth, but her insight and experiences will be so helpful to others and what's more be totally unique! Chanel, of course, wins top marks all round. The lovely assistant was the most helpful we have ever met and it is heart-warming to know there are some store assistants who treat people in wheelchairs with the respect and courtesy they deserve.

More importantly, they understand that women in wheelchairs also want to feel feminine and special – and wear nice perfume. I can remember the antiseptic hospital smells after my sense of smell came back and was thrilled when my friends brought in perfumes and scented moisturizers. I felt and looked like complete s*** but I hope I smelled wonderful!

This valuable support from stroke survivors like Chelle, makes me think of Gary Parkinson whose family members are looking beyond his disability to harness the same mind that has always been there. I was lucky enough to meet Gary and his wife Deborah when I visited Chelle at a neuro-rehabilitation centre in Lancashire. Unbeknown to me, Gary was in the room next room so I could chat to him and Deborah.

The former professional footballer was left severely disabled after a severe stroke in September 2010. The 43-year-old was a well-known player at Middlesbrough FC during the eighties and remained heavily involved in football in later years.

Middlesbrough manager Tony Mowbray was determined not to let Gary's sporting knowledge go to waste and in November last year decided to employ him as a talent scout for his old team. Gary quickly devised a ratings system with his wife Deborah that enables him to use his professional expertise to give his verdict on players.

I received a lovely message from Gary's niece Andrea which says she read my first book '*Running Free*', and said my story had '*made myself and my family open our minds a lot more to understand what my uncle (Gary Parkinson) is going through. He has the same condition. It has given us much more hope...'* and now Andrea, as a Facebook follower, is also aware of my Fighting Strokes charity. The Parkinson's daughter Chloe has also been in touch on Facebook.

When you read the next chapter you will realise just how many people contact me from around the world. I hope that Fighting Strokes continues to play an important role in fighting their cause. I have already received supportive emails from The Stroke Association (UK) and American Stroke Association and many others. Hopefully, more organisations around the world will also share information, news, medical research and case studies. I do believe that Fighting Strokes has the potential to help a great many people and have a global impact.

I just must add one sentence for Andy Davies and his amazing family.

Thanks for making January 17th one of my most special and heartwarming days this year!

Keep on fighting!

NB At the time of writing, Sunday January 29th 2012, I can share another entry on Andy's website.

Sunday January 29th 2010
Left arm and index finger!!!

Great news!!! Andy spelt out arm today only to show us that he was able to lift his arm up off the bed two inches. He also now has a flicker of voluntary movement in his left index finger. Thank You Lord. This is just a continuation of the recovery, which God has promised to complete.

And another positive blog message from:

Andy's Mum 1st February 2012
It is now a full three months since Andy's devastating brainstem stroke on 1st November 2011. Initially, he could not move any part of his body except his eyes and eyelids. He could not breathe without a ventilator; his heart rate, blood pressure and body temperature were out of control

and Andy was on life supporting ICU. Doctors could give us no assurance of any hope for even a partial recovery.

Today

Andy's vital processes are now stable, his heart and lung function is good; he now has good control over his head movement; he can swallow soft foods and liquids and is beginning to speak a few key words. He has flickers of movement in his right thumb, left index finger and can raise his left arm a few cm from the bed. Just yesterday Andy stood on the tilt table at 90° holding up his head and left arm. Thank you to all on the staff at QEHB who have helped Andy and the therapists who have worked so hard, helping him to achieve his goals to move, walk and talk again. Thank you to Kate Allatt and all the 'stroke fighters' who have given us all inspiration, advice and support having 'been there and come through' – you are really special people.

Fighting Strokes contact details

Kateallatt.com/fightingstrokes.org.

Please follow me on
linkedin/facebook-fighting strokes
or
twitter@fightingstrokes/youtube 'runmadkate'.

Note: charity registration 1143584

'I'm disabled!' (...If it means I am non-PC and queue jump!) I find a way to be a 'top mum' at Disney, June 2011.
© Kate Allatt

Disney World, June 2011.
© Kate Allatt

My first protégé Pete Coghlan (with Jade) Australia, August 2011. © Kate Allatt

My first headland walk to Trevone from Harlyn Sands, near Padstow in Cornwall, August 2011. © Kate Allatt

Gethin Jones with me and, Jaqui @ ITV's 'Holding out for a Hero'. © 12 Yard Productions

Our first quiet night in Majorca. September 2011 left to right Kate, Alison, Jaqui and Anita. © Kate Allatt

Feeling 'delicate' with Alison during our last night in Majorca, September 2011. © Kate Allatt

My punishing gym regime in the lead up to my 1 km run in the Percy Pud 10 KM race. With physiotherapist/ personal trainer/ counsellor/ friend Mike Lee, October 2011. © Kate Allatt

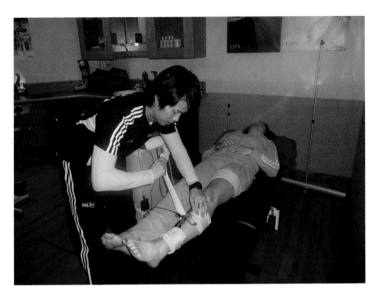

Mike Lee applying tape! November 2011. © *Kate Allatt*

Meeting Rt. Hon Nick Clegg MP (Deputy PM) at his Sheffield surgery, November 2011. © *Kate Allatt*

Run Mad Kate! The first time 'I got air!' November 2011.
© Kate Allatt

My top supporters – Mark and Alison at the Percy Pud race (even though Alison's Tee says, 'I don't do running!'). Every runner received a Xmas Pud and I won a special trophy!
© Cheryl Galsworthy

*Mike and I completing 1 km!
Thank God it's over! Percy
Pud, December 2011.*

© www.flaming photography.co.uk

*Running buddies! With
Alison at the Percy Pud
race, December 2011.*

© Cheryl Galsworthy

*Mark presents our kids with individual 'time with daddy'
tickets on Christmas Day 2011. (To see Peter Andre,
Diversity and the WWE Wrestlemania Revenge Tour in 2012).
Mark specially chose the gifts so each of the children could
spend time just with him.* © Kate Allatt

'I did it!' Running free on my beloved Blacka Moor.

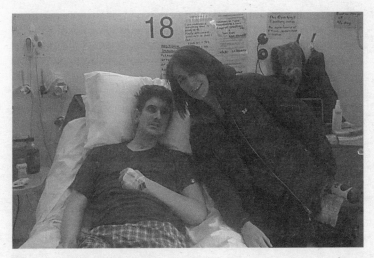

Keep on Fighting Andy!
I visit Andy Davies in hospital on January 17th 2012.

The future is bright... putting a rocket under the subject of stroke, with all the surrounding issues on BBC Breakfast TV on 14.3.12 with Bill and Sian.

Chapter 14 –
Thank you Mr. Zuckerberg!

When my girls' holiday to Majorca was over, and we had all overcome our first ever friendship tiff, I returned home to a huge pile of very encouraging emails and a very worried family.

It was great to see them, as they clearly missed me, but Mark's relief was palpable and only tempered by his concern over the size of my medical bill!

He had to pay it over the phone, which we would have to claim back and I looked sheepishly at him as he hugged me close to him. What I put him through! I could have perhaps taken more care of myself...it really wasn't my fault that my food went down the wrong way (though I could have slowed down a bit), and we both knew this.

Anyway, I blame my uncontrollably egocentric esophagus for being the catalyst in the late night colourful Vom-Com drama aboard the yacht. Never content to be a background extra as my disabilities came to the fore; it always managed to grab the starring role and take centre stage as discussed in previous chapters. Perhaps it was the indignation of being 'out of work' and 'resting' for all those months that led to it's most attention seeking performance to date; a dramatic grand finale. Those very nice Americans will certainly never forget the scene in their minds for a very long time I'm sure. Sorry guys!

As I settled down for the meal Mark had cooked – and my obligatory cup of Earl Grey – I promised I would take extra care with my food as Mark looked on nervously, then smiled. I think he was beginning to see the funny side of the story now I was back safe and sound, tanned and refreshed rather than frazzled. Though he was somewhat bemused by my temporary friendship fall-out – a first for me. Mark knows I always pride myself on having great loyal friends and am a great believer in hanging onto them.

That is why I am so pro-Facebook. One of the most amazing and popular social networking initiatives to date, and I think its co-founder Mark (all the best men are called Mark!) Zuckerberg is a complete star in my book.

I hesitated about opening up my Facebook account and Fighting Strokes page. I hadn't checked or posted on it in four days, which was a record. Would people have forgotten about me or thought I had given up on them?

I didn't need to worry was as my charity page was undated and actually functioning nicely without me. As I read the entries, I thought of how Mr. Zuckerberg had personally saved my life, which is no exaggeration.

To some, Facebook might be seen as a place for cyber bullying, illicit party organising or banal conversations, but for me it was anything but. It was my lifeline. It *really* was.

I first managed to open up my world from Osborne 4 back in May 2010. I only had use of my right index finger as my arm was balanced on a cushion on a table.

At the nurses station I would interact with the world and break the solitary life of hospital.

Posting my status updates to my blog – beatinglockedinsyndrome – not only broke my lonely hours; it also appealed to my competitive nature.

You see, I used to post on my status every time I achieved something new for the first time, whether it be sitting for one minute, blowing a ping-pong ball with a straw without having to hold my nose or tying my shoe laces or going upstairs for the first time.

I was like a toddler, having to learn everything again – pooing, writing, controlling my bladder, sitting, swallowing, forming letters, brushing my hair and teeth, dressing, making my bed, cooking, etc. (I *love* to cook and one friend, Ally, was quite touched to see me – much later, shuffling around to serve up a Sunday roast in the early days of my arrival back home when I had progressed to crutches.)

Each time I posted Facebook comments, I received back enormous encouragement that I would want to ensure I exceeded the following day. It was a *huge* motivator.

I was competing with me, but I wanted to continually impress my 'fans' to get more posts from them the next day. Mark said, 'bet you can't get 500 fans!' My thought was, 'you're on!' and within a month I got over 1000!

Facebook also gave me the anonymity I needed. I was faceless, non-disabled, and 'normal' and I liked hiding behind my red laptop or nurse's computer.

I was able to participate in the real 'cyber' world and I had company. The fact that Mark and I would often row online, not realising everyone used to tune in especially to read our real-life soap opera exchanges!

I quit my *beatinglockedin* page because I really wanted to hand over the baton, because I was now 'normal' right?

This is what I wrote on 2nd August 2011.

Thankyou from the bottom of my heart! But its time for others...

I've said it before, but I CANNOT tell you how much your cyber support, encouragement and kind words have got me here. We know how difficult I was, we know how single minded I was (I hope less so now!!), or how hard I worked every minute of every day. Its true to say that, getting better for me, was and is, an obsession.

When I refer to Facebook 'saving my life', it quite literally did. Genuinely.

My first stroke anniversary Feb 2011

You will never know how many countless times in hospital that I looked forward to posting on Facebook, (with my only moving 'index right finger'), as my right arm rested on a pillow or table, whilst I stayed at the nurses station computer for hours on end. I developed the worst pressure sores on my arm!

Facebook wasn't just inane or tittle-tattle for me, nor was it for the countless people who joined Facebook because they wanted to follow my daily progress. Facebook was serious as:

a. It opened up the world from my 'bubble' of Osborne 4 but...

b. I Had a basic need in me, that I needed to impress you all, (I'm a competitive person. 'Really?' I hear!!) I would work so hard in my therapy sessions, just to be sure that I had something pretty amazing to post to you all in this blog everyday but;

c. This all really, really motivated me to get out of my hell, out of hospital and back with my family where I belonged.

My book 'Running Free' was everything I wanted – a legacy to my kids (who wouldn't ever really 'know' me, if I died young). It was cathartic for me (and still is). It has also provided a great insight into the mind of someone (albeit a blunt, Northern lass with 'choice' language) and, I hope, a useful 'read' for patients, caregivers and health professionals. . The bonus is that the feedback is that you all seem to quite like it. (Quite remarkable really, as I just said how it was for me and from MY perspective from what I experienced.) In retrospect, whilst my version of the story was totally true as I saw it, it may have been 'balanced' out by stuff happening outside of my control or for that matter my knowledge at the time. But I wholeheartedly stand by my account and what I knew at the time. But the only additional emphasis I would have made in my book (as I found out too late) was how my husband, Mark, really changed the early course of my life (and opportunity to respond to my intensive therapy) as it was his decision to send me to rehab initially as opposed to the 'normal' pathway of post-stroke care. (They tried to make me go to Rehab and I said 'yes, yes! yes!' but I shouldn't have!)

Since I left hospital, and with Mike's constant help, knowledge and support, I had my second 'stroke' (great pun huh?!!) of luck. I could never have imagined I'd get his level of help last October 2010 when I went to Esporta armed with my cheeky business plan. Its been just me and him ever since! Wow, has he done wonders to tame and harness my bloody mindedness and wilfulness!

I really feel with almost full charitable status & new website (end August 2011), with our strategy and my new dual career, that life is good but its time to let my stroke play second fiddle to others who need and deserve the attention more. I think other people – patients, health professionals and carers need the limelight. I promise to do all I can to ensure they know everything they need to know on stroke recovery therapies and developments and how we promise to work with other charities and the NHS to get change as well as promote the good things I received too.

I am lucky, I never forget that. Therefore, if you want news, developments, technology or to share your story please become a Fan of 'Fighting Strokes' http://www. facebook.com/home.php#!/fightingstrokes.org

I have received so many Facebook comments, emails and messages of support. I decided to take random selections which show the views of those who have followed me on Facebook and many reveal that strokes can happen to ANYONE!

To protect the identities of those I couldn't email for permission to use, I have changed their names out of respect to them. After all, they are real people with real life stories and I feel SO honoured they have written to me. I truly consider them friends. Where I have had the express permission to use names, I have retained their original identities. All email messages I received from Facebook appear in the way I originally received them and have therefore not been edited. All views of my Facebook friends give others an insight into what stroke survivors, their carers, relatives and friends are going through every day all over the world. That is the incredible power of Facebook!

Oliver (UK)
This is what my funny nurse Oliver wrote on 28th September 2010.

Hi Kate. Thanks for your very kind words. And thanks, too, for allowing us to be part of your journey for the past 8 months It really has been an honour to have been part of it and to witness your strength and determination. You say you may have been 'somewhat difficult'....well, I wouldn't say that... You have a very strong character and won't take second best. In being like this, you have progressed so far – and will continue to progress. We will see you in December for your run. I will hold you to a drink at Abbeydale some time soon!

Take care Kate
Oliver

Allyson (USA)

One of the earliest messages I had was from 'Across the Pond' from Allyson Lindberg Tyson in November 2010 and I was touched to see she had typed LOL in her text (That's the spirit!) Her message read:

Hello my new friend! I wanted to give you a quick update on my brother, John Lindberg. Last Tuesday night they thought he had a pulmonary embolism, but he 'just' had bad pneumonia. It turned out to be staph, but at least not the bad staph! He also has a yeast infection in his lungs and mouth, which hurts him, lots of blisters, etc. Anyway, the doctor came in and John turned his head looked at him, opened and shut his mouth. Show off! LOL. He squeezed the doctor's hand with his right hand and moved his right foot. The doctors are amazed by him. We have done tons of research, and we think John is the ONLY patient in Texas in LIS. They probably don't even know truly what to make of him! But they told him that as soon as he can stick out his tongue that they'll do a swallow test and get rid of the tracheotomy. That would be amazing. Well, best news was the doctor came in and for the first time actually said he was hopeful that John would regain quite a bit. He said that he thought it might take about a year, but his nerves are finding new pathways around the damaged area of his brainstem. He said John's MRI shows that there is just a very thin slice of the brainstem that is totally occluded. He said there are other areas that are halfway occluded, but that doesn't cause these problems. He said even though it is a thin slice, it was enough to cause LIS but that since it is so thin, the nerves can find new pathways and he said that is what they are doing right now, which is why he can move somewhat. Isn't that awesome news? Well I went to see him (he is still 2 1/2 hours from home) yesterday and I read him your messages. You inspire him so much. I told him that your plans were to travel and speak about LIS and I said, 'John, you want to travel with Kate and tell everybody about this? and he blinked YES emphatically! I CANNOT WAIT for the day that I can fly him over to meet you. It will happen, I promise. Have a wonderful day Kate and big hugs to you. I'll send you more updates soon. Hopefully he is moving to rehab in a few days! Allyson Lindberg Tyson.

14 November 2010
Kate Allatt

That's fantastic news! I am so thrilled for your family friends and for John! Keep working hard – you'll do it! Think of how many battles you've had and overcome, it won't win! Joining me to spread awareness. Sounds good, only 1 on Texas no less!'
Good luck, this really spurs me!
Have been having a flat weekend, NOT! its just picked up!
Kate
xx

13 December 2010
Allyson Lindberg

Hi Kate! I hope you are doing better and better each and every day! John is back at the home getting therapy and he actually got up in a wheelchair last week for the first time! They are testing him tomorrow to possibly remove trach, and he is happy about that. He had a small seizure the other day, and they said it was 'normal'?? Did you have that happen? Tuesday, Wednesday, and Thursday he was soooo happy, laughing, smiling and lifting his right leg up and down off the bed. Then Friday he started getting quiet and today he has slept all day and blinked that he had too much medicine. They didn't give him any. I'm scared, I wonder if he is having more seizures of if this is just part of the process. I know it takes a long time and I need to be patient, but I love him so much and want him to get well!

Did you go through the same things? It has been 2 1/2 months since stroke and LIS. Oh, by the way, he is swallowing on his own 100% and can lift his head up off the pillow all the way to his shoulders now. He can open his mouth very wide and move his tongue and is still looking laterally. The arms aren't moving but he can still squeeze a little with his right hand. I read somewhere that arms were the last to get back, was that your situation? Do you remember? Sorry for all the questions, but you are the only one I know who was in his same situation.

Thank you so very much and I hope you have the Merriest Christmas EVER!

XOXOXO,

Allyson Lindberg Tyson

15 December 2010
Kate Allatt

What do you mean by seizures? When I had my trachy out they wanted to be sure I had a strong cough reflex. They were tempted in reinstate. Over my dead body, I was slowly for the first time getting my body back! I understand his smiles!

Have you been tested to see if his stroke is genetic? If its not, he's no more than you of having another one. It's a blood test. My nerves are jumpy especially in the mornings/night. I suffer terribly with restless legs at night. I urge you to demand speech therapy, occupational therapy, along with physio. 3 hrs per day, plus him

170

working/practicing all day alone, his pathway is there, build on this he will be very weak at first.

Squeezing once or twice at first only. I think it's a bit like the funfair; it's all I knew and all he needs to know. When you hit the hammer to make the bell ring at the top, eventually it reaches the bell. Keep trying all the time.

My arms were after my legs, always my priority, never wanted to be in a wheelchair! Then my arms, then my speech. I don't believe your body can doing all 3 at once, but keep practicing anyway. I really hope this helps?

Firstly, get the therapy! Everyday each for one hour! Give John an important date in a year's time he must be at/attend and work towards that date. Cross the days off.

I have just recommended these at another sufferer's family. Helpful?

Exercises x 10 of each, 5 x per day: smile with lips ...closed. Open your mouths as wide as you can, stretch your muscles. Try and touch the inside roof of your mouth with your tongue. Tuck in your tongue behind your upper front teeth. Stick your tongue out as far as you can, trying to touch a mouth sponge, mine were pink, dry sponges on sticks. Eventually try a dry chilled (with ice cubes) t-spoon x 10 to encourage the swallow reflex. Only if know you are not silently aspirating move onto tspoons of icy water 5 x only. I had nothing for weeks, before the flickers came, keep trying, use mirror for him so he can see and encourage the pathways. Give him lots of encouragement and do during visits.

Kate

5 January 2012
Allyson Lindberg

Dearest Kate,

I hope you remember me. My brother, John Lindberg, had a brain-stem stroke October 3, 2010 and became Locked-in. You have been a source of inspiration to him and my entire family since this incident.

I purchased your book for my Nook and have been reading it the past few days. I have cried, cheered and laughed through the entire thing. I am going to read it to John next week when I can see him because I am home sick with the flu. I am hoping that your words will inspire him to fight, fight, and fight!!! In America, if you do not have health insurance, you get just the basic of care. Since he couldn't afford coverage, he has gotten barely anytherapy of any kind since his stroke 15 months ago. All of these things, he has done on his own. He can smile, cry, laugh, but still no speech.

He can turn his head from side-to-side and that is how he calls the nurse. He can squeeze your hand with both hands, but it is kind of a hit and miss effort.

If we are arguing in his room, he will kick the end of the bed, ha ha. But no trunk control cannot really move fingers individually yet, although I have seen him do it in the past. Cannot lift his arms or anything. He can cough and clear his own airway, which I think is remarkable. He has no catheter, and calls the nurse when he has to wee and she rolls him over and holds the urinal for him. I think that is s huge milestone, don't you?

I am going to encourage him to try some things that you outlined in your book. I feel like you and I are old friends and I definitely ant to meet you some day. If I ever get to England, you are the first person I meet! And if you come back to America, please let me know. I will fly to wherever you are!!!!! If you get a chance, I would love a reply with some thoughts and even maybe a message for John. Tell Mark I am impressed with him, what a wonderful human being. My sister-in-law, Kim, has been just as amazing with John. Looks like you 2 hit the jackpot when you picked your spouses!!

I will close now, but will definitely keep you updated on his progress and condition. Kate, thank you for showing the courage and conviction to write this book and bring awareness to LIS. You are amazing!!!

Much love,
Allyson Lindberg

5 January 2012
Kate Allatt

Hello Allyson
So lovely to hear from you.

John has made so much progress and with the minimum support you are all getting, that is no mean feat! How is his chest now?

No catheter is fabulous too. He has to retrain everything and that's so noteasy with the help you get. I hope we will meet in the same way I also feel bad for my 'stroke swearing' in my first book! My new book 'Gonna fly Now!' is a different read charting my highs and crashing lows with another infamous girly boat trip! (It will be available on kindle or itunes or paperback). It's funny and sad, shoot from the hip style!

John sounds like he has a lot of positive signs and maybe I can help if I know which parts of his body are his priority? I know all strokes are different, but my mum was told by a neurologist that 'if I manage to makenew voluntary (as opposed to involuntary) neural pathways (by 'willing' otherwise known as brain plasticity) those pathways never stop working.

However, like with a broken limb that have been 'potted' for 3 months or more, the muscles temporarily waste away and therefore cant physically move the bones. So game on, everything to still play for.

happy new year to you all.
kate x

Sent: 07 February 2012 16:10
Back in April 2011, I received an email from Daniel Hodson.

Daniel Hodson (UK)

My name Daniel Hobson and I live in Marple, Stockport. I know all about your story and would like to take this opportunity to say how truly amazing you are and what an inspiration you are to others in this situation. Which brings me to my reason for contacting you. My best friend lives in Australia and has had a massive stroke at 33 and is recovering. You may have heard his name is Pete Coghlan and his partner is Jade D'souza. They are both managing very well with this life changing experience. I would like to use you to help motivate, push, and inspire Pete in his time of need. I would like to start by meeting you to have one of your books signed for him so I can get it to him in Oz. Pete like yourself is going to dedicate his life to help others in a similar situation and I would like to be the one to bring you all together to help others. I didn't want to add you as a friend without asking first. I can be contacted via Facebook.

My profile picture shows us all when times were good, Pete and Jade are on the left and I am third from the right. We all pray that the next good time pictures are of Pete walking down the aisle, which has been postponed until he can. This is his fuel to marry his girl.

I subsequently met Daniel with his girlfriend in Sheffield in June 2011. I started emailing them continuously, with my tips, based upon my experiences and my advice. His relationship with Pete in Australia reminded me of Alison's own unshakable commitment and loyalty to me and I was going to explore every avenue possible to affect a change on the opposite side of the world.

It transpired that Pete's father's brother, who lived in Thailand, was a Rotarian. He discovered me through the mutual 'secret' connections via my Rotarian father-in-law Kev in Southport.

Pete had hope, self-belief and the 'prove-it-wrong' attitude in bucket loads. My story inspired and empowered him to take control over his recovery and break records. The emails to and from Daniel were so encouraging as he smashed every record and blew out the rulebook on brainstem stroke recovery. I sent him my first book, and my picture was displayed in his hospital room to continually inspire him.

He even made every nurse read my book in Australia, because I said things, often bluntly, how he'd been feeling.

On 6th August 2011, I received Pete's message on Facebook.

Peter Coghlan (Australia)

Hi Kate,

Pete here, thankyou for you book. It it was my case all over, it gave me alot of hope for the future i am presently at home on my first overnight leave, i am still weak and working with one arm as the otherone moves but mostly from the shoulder really, i cant wait for it to work but i hate waiting for anything, my question for you, if you dont mind is did your arm come on faster on one side first and if so how long. i am writing a diary every day or so, in the hope to also write a book some day, would you be intrested in reading it or will it bring to many memories back, either way i want to keep in contact with you if you dont mind. Its been 19 weeks and i have been told its fast but it seems so slow, what a torture, please can you cheer me on with a few word of hope as your the only one who knows what its like.I can stand but walking is scary i need two physios i am currently rocking a walking stick back and forward for hours every night in the hope that it builds what little muscle i have in my right arm, I also have no gag reflex and have had 4 chest infections i tried the toothbrush, when out of sight of the nurses with my girl and nothing happend will it come or am i in shit? i am hoping to build my legs up so they are strong enough to pump my heart faster and open my lungs. in order to help with my speech what do think?, I just broke my record this week and did a whopping 30 ks on the exercise bike and they told my family I would never move from my neck down, shows you what they know hey! you and I must be made of different stuff.All tips welcome any one whos beat this gets my ultimate respect, I too want to marry at the end of this shit i saw your pics of your wedding vows renewal, so now i hope thats me soonish, any way i can talk, (everyone used to call me have a chat) so best stop before I dont stop, hope you reply soon thanks from Aussie Pete take care of yourself would love to see more pics of your family in disneyland, Jade just said she will show them to me on her facebook, thanx once again xxx.

And here was my response,

Hello fellow fighter! I heard you were watching Rocky recently, how funny! Where to start.... Of course I'd love to read your book, my advice is to log everything, on a timeline of events (so you get the order right), think about half a dozen key characters – friends, family who will appear throughout the book. (The others will be cameo mentions, otherwise you will overload the reader!) think if your dark times (icu in my book, doesn't go half enough in terms if how bad it was for me, but i couldn't go there any more than i did) and some bits which were hopefully humorous! Start making detailed notes, then all you are doing is linking the events.! What inspired you to fight this total shit? Both High and low points? Your arm – my left side was really f*****. it's still slower, my reactions are slower, but improving. But not now far behind my right side. Insist on electrical therapy like F.E.S. (Functional Electric Stimulation) to activate new pathways every day. (Bit like Frankenstein but it worked for me!) you are a fighter. You are bound to get down, I still do, but u must know that you are progressing so fast, like me. Hang in there, just imagine, we could take on the world!!!! It won't be long and you too will get married, she's a good lady!! (Although Mark says, our marriage is longer than the prison sentence he would have got for murder!) Pete, you are on the home run, you will soon be 'normal' supping that beer! The gag reflex should return. (in my opinion) the best exercise to stimulate is swallowing practice. Have you tried a dry, chilled t-spoon? To stimulate a swallow, safetly? The cold, dry t-spoon stimulates a swallow and u minimize any risks of silently aspirating? Keep in touch, be strong little Rocky. You will get there. Allow yourself down days, just bloody well sort yourself out for next week! u know that you are already doing far more than they expected, keep amazing them and

*surprising them. Above all never let up with your practice!!
Big hugs Kate xxxxx*

Clearly Pete hadn't lost his sense of humour either!

*'Thanks for getting back to me, it means a lot. I am in
my four bed bedroom and the man behind has just shit
himself, O what joy!'*

Then his fiancée Jade wrote me this after Pete walked
out of hospital – YouTube Pete talking from Shenton Park
Perth posted on 27/9/11.

*My name is Jade, I am Peter Coghlan's Partner and I
just wanted to write a huge thankyou for meeting Dan
and Ange the other day and signing your book. Everyday
since Pete had his stroke I have been telling him what
an inspiration you are. You have given us so much
hope and Pete the determination he required to fight
through when the doctors left him stripped of everything.
Today Pete has been on the exercise bike for 15 minutes
and is progressing so fast (although he does not think it
is fast enough) Reading and watching your video's has
shown me so much that until the other day I could only
relay in words to Pete, but for the first time the other
day I was able to show them to him, he was amazed to
see your recovery through all these stages and I want to
thank you for sharing this with the rest of the world, I
told Pete I would love for you to both meet one day and
stand tall together. I have printed the picture of you,
Dan and Ange and he tells everyone about you daily.
Thanks once again for everything and hope we get to meet
you one day in the future, keep up the good work, you are
amazing.*

All our love Jade & Pete XXXXX

Tony Coghlan (UK)

Dear Kate.

I just wanted to thank you for being such a wonderful friend and support to my nephew Pete in Australia. It was my wife reading an article about you in a magazine here on the South coast that prompted me to try to contact you through your father-in-law in Southport Rotary. The rest you know! We are so impressed by his progress and by his indomitable spirit and I know a lot of this is down to you. It is said the only people who know what you are going through are the people who have trod the path themselves--- need I say more?

I hope you are also continuing with your good progress and that your families too are well.

Kindest regards and many thanks again,
Tony Coghlan

Other people that I have helped since my stroke are Mark and Amy Ellis from Chesterfield. He was just 23 years old and suffered a brainstem stroke with locked in syndrome.

He was told he had plateaued or rather that the community stroke care budget had run out.

I visited them both back in October 2010. Here is what Mark said,

'It was great to meet you and your husband, you are both great people. Thanks to you both you got me more motivated and I won't stop my new mouth exercises, straw and ping pong ball and my own physio xxx'

Amy also said,

'Morning Kate, can I just say thank you for your Fighting Strokes page, which has brought new meaning to Mark's life. He is constantly talking to others on there and has given him the confidence boost he needed, as he is now

*so positive. Thank you so much 4 the positive help u give.
U R an angel sent to help others.'*

Over in America word is getting out with Bob Miller,
Creator of 'Strokes Suck' and a survivor of two strokes.

Bob Miller, San Diego, America.

*Hi Kate, your story is nothing short of amazing. In our
(Strokes Suck) weekly newsletter, we have a feature called
'incredible breakthrough. This is for someone who has
had a recovery breakthrough and/or is doing something
to give back to the community. You most certainly would
qualify. ...In fact, like an ultra marathoner, you are an
'ultra survivor.'*

Strokes Suck is a worldwide international movement
with the motto 'Give, Help, Inspire'. They believe that
Strokes Suck 'but' there are things that you can do to
improve your life.

An inspirational stroke survivor and runner, Ernie,
certainly inspired me to run again.

Ernie Kasper (America)

*Hey there, I am the guy who made the video BELIEVE.
Well I guess I am also the runner and stroke survivor.
Right now I am running 7 miles in 70 cities. Big hugs!!!!*

Mum of four-year-old Locked-in daughter (UK)

*My daughter was a healthy 4 year old until one evening,
whist playing with her cousins, she suddenly came down
stairs holding her head and screaming... within 15mins
she was unconscious and being taken to A&E. Her first CT
scan showed a massive brain bleed, which we now know
to be caused by an AVM. She was air lifted (more than
100 miles) to hospital and underwent surgery through the
night. We have seen 2 miracles so far and we are praying
for a third. The first was that she survived the helicopter
journey; the second was that she came through surgery*

and we are now expecting the third, recovery. A week after surgery she was still sedated and an MRI showed extensive stroke damage to the cerebellum and the brain stem, the doctors were unsure she could survive such extensive trauma. However it is now 11 weeks since her bleed and stroke and she is still with us. Not only that, but she is awake, her eyes move and she is able to communicate 'Yes' by rolling her eyes up, she can focus on books and smile at the silly things we say. She can move all her limbs to different degrees and is learning to wiggle her fingers. With good hospital physiotherapy, she is beginning to experience the sensation of standing and sitting in specialist chairs. Our daughter remains fully ventilated at the moment, but we have seen how far she has come in 11 weeks and are hopeful about the future. Straight away Kate had plenty of advice and came to visit her. She appeared to like the idea of being in 'Kate's Gang' and we're still practising sticking out our tongue as a result. Kate has been an inspiration and encouragement to us as parents, that all things are possible and her determination has encouraged us to speak out about our hopes for her future. We now have clearer goals and a stronger emphasis on rehabilitation thanks to Kate's support.

Amanda (Canada)

Dear Kate,

Want to let you know you have been an inspiration to our family. Our son, Stephen, had a catastrophic brain stem (pons area) stroke on Oct. 15th. His prognosis was very poor, 'Locked-in Syndrome' at the best. We began researching LIS and found your site and read the news article from the November article in Sheffield Telegraph to Steve. Shortly after, he began responding and began waking up. He is in a rehabilitation facility and engaged in speech/swallowing, physical and occupational therapies, moving all limbs now and talking (no voice, due to trach/ so we are struggling to read his lips) He is still on a vent, hospitalized this past wk. for GI bleeding (had to have transfusions) and has a very serious cornea ulcer.

There is a long, hard road ahead, but Steve is very committed to his recovery.

Thank you and keep running!

Blessings,

(Stephen's parents)

Received your book from Waterstone's.... read it non-stop, now reading it to Steve, who can identify with your journey so well. (He was also thrilled to be mentioned on pg. 193!)

George (UK)

George said,'Hello Kate, my name is George I emailed you about 3 months ago, thanks for the advice you gave me. I have just started to get some slight movement in my right arm, which was paralysed, and some controlled shaking, can you give me any tips or advice to get it moving anymore. All the best and thanks very much'.

Tina (America)

Dear Kate,

My family and I here in New York have read with great interest and hope your remarkable story of recovery from 'Locked-in syndrome'. My dear niece (45 years old, with 2 children, 4 and 6) was stricken on Christmas night with a brain stem stroke and is so affected. The doctor's hold little hope for any meaningful recovery. Would you share with us the location of your stroke? Was it in the brain stem or some other part of your brain? We are grateful for any information you would share with us. I wish you continued improved health and thank you for anything you are willing to share about your condition.

Sincerely,

Tina

Justine (Canada)

Hi Kate,

First off all I am very happy for you and your family that you were able to get out of it. I am sure it must have taken a lot of energy and hard work. When my 15 year old son and I started reading your book, it felt as if we were ready about a female version on my husband, around 54). He could never just do things either without giving it 200% and he was also planning to climb mount Kilimanjaro. We have two children, 15 and 12.

According to my husband's medical file, he has locked in syndrome after a brain stem stroke back in November, 2010 but he started getting sensation back slowly into his body a couple of months after the stroke. He can now move his legs, feet, arms, and hands and head a bit, although it is small movements. I do not believe that he is locked in anymore and that he needs to go somewhere where he can start intense rehab, which unfortunately in is not available here. There is lots for children under 18 or for seniors, but for someone that still has a trach and according to his file has locked in syndrome there is nothing.... all they can offer is long term care which will not get you more than 2 or 3 times per week physio of about 45 minutes each. Even speech therapy is only about 15 minutes, twice a week. My husband has yelled to the doctors 'I want the trach out' but they are scared as it is maybe to early to take it out.

Do you have any suggestions for him when it comes to the trach and do you know of any good rehab facilities that would take out of country patients?

Alice (Denmark)

Hello :-) My name is Alice. I am a 50-year old woman from Denmark. 13 years ago I got Locked-in-syndrome. I am paralyzed from the neck down and I can't speak. I have a personal assistant to help me during the day. I live with my husband and daughter. Is there anybody else with

Locked-in-syndrome here, who would like to get in touch by writing? If from Denmark, we could also meet.

Bridget (UK)

You are an inspiration to both young and old victims of stroke. As a runner myself and recent experience of major stroke in the family you are amazing. You have captured so much in your book that touches a lot of chords – well done you and I hope you go from strength to strength in you campaign and life.

Selina (Brazil)

Hi Kate, I read his story and said everything about the Locked-in syndrome, I had Guillain Barre Syndrome August-September 2005, our story was too similar in fact to leave the hospital walking (and no one believed I would do it) but I did! Also fought against the sagging muscle and strength to the nerves and muscles. And so it will not be able to ever stop noticing my physiotherapy. I'm glad I found you. It seems I was reading my story. Thank you for good news about you. A peck of Brazilian friend.' Selina.

Audrey (America)

I was very excited to read about your book and hope to read it soon. I am a physical therapist in inpatient rehab in the United States. I work with people with stroke, traumatic brain injury, and spinal cord injury and have a dream of starting a walking and running club for them for when they discharge. I was wondering how running is going for you now. What sorts of things did you and did therapists do that have made starting and continuing to run easier, and what have been the barriers? What advice do you have for me or also for my patients (practically speaking or in terms of perspective and hope)? Thanks for writing this book! – Audrey

My reply to Audrey.

Wow. Brilliant!

I would say a few things (not least that the second edition or Running Free has a helpful appendix!) I had to have time to start the fight with a few 'triggers' that helped me turn the 'fight' on (about 16 weeks) But when my 'spark' came back, all hell broke loose with my focus, obsession and strong personal goals (I will walk again!) The idea of being in a wheelchair for life with someone wiping my own butt was totally abhorrent to me as a previous fell runner, as was not taking a full participatory role in my kids lives. Observer I never was! So psychologically it's so important, as is full cognitive function. Instant, early physio, occupational and speech therapy, it was unprecedented. 1 hour each a day from week 12 after my brainstem stroke, full blockage. Prior to that I was given 20 mins a day physio in ICU. For families, sure some people don't recover. Some patients believe the bleak prognosis doctors paint. Some caregivers are so convinced of this prognosis, they receive from doctors, that they don't raise hopes or patients' potentials in my experience. Doctors saved my life. Fact. Brilliant. But they also made mistakes, either that or they don't fully understand this condition and the potentials. Not least that they said to my husband, that I wouldn't walk, talk or swallow again. I do. Sure, doctors can paint the worst case and unfortunately and statistically paint the worst outcome, but some people DO make it, against the odds. I am an example, maybe small, but it has happened. There is hope. This antithesis, this possibility with 'real' people should be quoted as a possibility too. I hope more people do what I did. Similarly, not everyone has the 'fight' and, I'm afraid, 'give up'

Hope you enjoy the book.

Clare (UK)

I lost my mum on new years day after she suffered a brain stem stroke in July 2011. She was left with locked in syndrome. Your book helped me understand what she must have been going through and spurred me on to try and help her communicate as much as possible, although sadly my mum didn't make too much progress we had fun trying. Thank you for writing the book and giving me the opportunity to give my wonderful mum the best that I could for the last 5 months of her life xxx

Fabio (Brazil)

Hi, my name is Jason and I'm 17 years old, you do not know me, I'm from Brazil, I read your story in a newspaper on the Internet today and was thrilled with her life. You are a true heroine. I am recovering from a broken collarbone. When I was broke so sad because I want to serve in the army, but as I broke this bone my chances of being admitted declined. But seeing your story I realized how my problems are insignificant. Their challenges have been infinitely greater and you overcame them with faith that few have. I'm sorry if there are many mistakes in this text, is that I do not speak English, I'm using google translate. But the only thing I want you to know is that you are already a winner and that her story serves as a motivation for many, regardless of country or language.
    God enlighten you during your journey.
    Of: a mere a boy
    To: a heroine.

In the run up to my December 20111 Percy Pud Dec race I received these Facebook comments from friends in response to my post which read...

Perhaps my next goal should be more work to build my 'real' as opposed to cyber relationships. It's too easy for me to continue the solitary life and my thoughts that I was forced into ICU (and pretty much ever since after) Of course; there have been comical exceptions, with friends and family, before and after I left hospital.
    But I should not hide behind my computer screen, or phone, out of view, at home. I need to force myself out in

the big wide world, not just like I do confidently for my worthwhile charity, but confidently for ME personally too. It's time to get and feel fully integrated back into society and stop hiding.

Sue Sandars

Keep going at it Kate, you/we do not hide behind screens, its a means of communication and spreading the word of stroke awareness in younger people and LIS, for some its their only way of contact, you've been working bloody hard as I have to get where we are, because we want to (thank you Billie Piper!) Because we want to get back to where we were pre stroke, and we are getting there not as quick as we may want but just look where we've got, and what we've done, be proud lady be proud - thanks Heather Small!

Stephanie (Dore, UK)

Well said! I have been stuck in for the last few months not able to drive or walk very far. Nowhere near the trauma you have been through but not going out a lot has made me a bit of a recluse!

Lizzie (UK)

I challenge thee to get in Rocky and come see me for a boozy night in!?...;) Xx

When I heard from Deborah Parkinson I was very iterested in what she had to say about her husband Gary, a well-known footballer with LIS.

Deborah Parkinson (UK)

Wow! wow! wow! You are such an inspiration Kate. Well done on your superb strength and recovery.......
I don't know how you would feel Kate about meeting up some time with me I am much more of an eye contact

kind of person who prefers to speak to people in person instead of through technology. I would love to try and help in some way to support your plight to highlight locked in syndrome.
Bye for now
Deborah Parkinson

I received another email from Deborah on Friday 3rd February 2012.

Hi Kate
It so nice to hear from you and great to see your charity taking off you are incredible and I know that you give such inspiration and hope to all us families out there living with strokes/locked in syndrome.
I hadn't heard about Mark from Chesterfield but again it's a heart breaking story but Mark has got determination and fight along with the support of his wife which he so needs. Well done too on your radio 2 interview on Wednesday thanks for the mention. Finally Gary is really enjoying scouting for players for Middlesbrough Football club he has been encouraged by this involvement its great for Gary to be kept involved.
Take care of yourself Kate first and foremost and look forward to seeing you soon

Regards Deborah x

I have met Deborah and Gary and they are helping get the message out those stroke survivors and their families need to stay positive. (Gary, as stated above is a former Middlesbrough FC football player who has recently been taken on as football talent scout for his old Middlesbrough team and uses eye movements in his ratings system to help management pick players).

Andrea (UK)

I was so inspired by you today talking to jeramy Vine...I shed tears hearing your story...what a fighter..I kept thinking of a scene in Kill Bill :).

Victoria (UK)

'Hello, I am just in the middle of reading your book and wanted to say that I find your courage remarkable and I am so glad you have made such a good recovery. I also think you have some fantastic friends. Victoria.'

One Facebook entry made me cry as I remembered when I first moved my thumb.

Elizabeth (UK)

Kate I am reading your book to my mum who is locked in and yesterday she moved her thumb and ring finger after 7 months of nothing. We both cried. Thank you for giving us some hope. Elizabeth.

I wrote this reply to a man called John whose mum is Locked-in. I hope this advice will be beneficial for a great many people.

John,
   I really am so sorry for your mum and the rest of the family and friends.
   I am sorry for the delay with this.
   Your mum is a fighter, and she's already proved that, I am sure her spirit will not remain broken, mine didn't.
   My words of advice based on my experiences would be:
   You never lose a voluntary neural pathway, but muscles WILL fatigue in the early weeks and months. This means that if your mum can make a deliberate movement to

order, than she will not lose that and has everything to play for.

It will be bloody hard work in rehab.

What is her ultimate goal?

There will be lots of small steps to get there. Remember, you can't eat an elephant in one go!

Stay focused and positive on the very small areas of progression each week.

Ask for functional electric stimulation

Ensure that you have their treatment plans in writing and ask for reviews with all the therapists, as against targets each fortnight.

Try and establish if your mum is cognitively normal, i.e. understands things and see to what level she can try and communicate back. This may be blinking, or rolling her eyes up and down or twitching a finger slightly or looking at a piece of paper with the answer she wants to give on.

Think of her environment. Are the nurses turning her TV on? Does she have an iPod docking station? Does she want fresh air?

Is she scared, bored, hot, cold, moved often enough, sleeping at night?

How are they going to manage her trachi weaning over time?

Is she wearing foot and hand splints?

So many questions.

Best wishes,

Kate.

Mike sent back this lovely message, which follows. I can totally relate to his reference relating to 'poohing out a watermelon.' I am not making light of it – very painful when your body goes through such turmoil. it is really shocking what you have to cope with. This email lifted my spirits when I heard how motivated his mum is and able to laugh – I love the ACDC comment. (Great-no whale music!) Mike sounds like a fun, upbeat son to have around and his daughter sounds wonderful! I wish his mum well.

John (UK)

Thank you so much for the reply, AND thank you so much for writing your book, it has been a huge help. My mom went through a few situations that your book helped us with this week. Pooing out a watermelon and thinking the nurses are killing her, since I read the book I was able to understand her stomach pain and talk with her about it and with the nurse be aware and hear her out. I showed her your book and assured her that she can beat this and her current situation can and will get better. I saw a huge sigh of relief on her face and she has been motivated ever since...SO THANK YOU

As for improvement, we are now on week four and she can move her lips and tongue completely so we don't need to use the letter chart, lip reading time. Her right hand and right leg have good movement. We took her outside yesterday for the first time in her wheelchair, which she loved. Our challenges are that she is very impulse (shave my head, move me to another hospital...) we find that the next day she will not bring it up anymore.

Socially, she is right there...able to laugh (through a trach is a scary sight) show her classic faces or expression, love and be sad. My daughter sang her all of the Christmas songs she is going to sing at her Christmas play which my mom loved. I also played her some ACDC on her ipad to get her pumped up for physiotherapy. I set a goal with her after your suggestion, which was to get the trach out and work hard enough to get to the point of being able to move to a great rehab centre so she can really kick ass. I find when she gets sad she turns down therapy, which can't happen if she has goals.

I would consider you very hardcore after reading your book, physically and mentally. My mom is the same, pushes herself to the brink each day physically and mentally. I know being strong is a huge advantage at beating locked in and I am glad she and us can look to you as an example.

Anthony (UK)

Hi Kate. I'm reading your book Running Free about your stroke and recovery, and wanted to say how inspiring it is for me as the family carer of my stroke survivor wife. My wife suffered a brain haemorrhage and stroke back in 2000 and is now learning to walk again with the aid of FES after 11 years in a wheelchair. I got her assessed as a demo patient by taking her to a Physiofunction health professionals training day in Coventry. Then it took 6 months to get our local health board approval. She also has a significant cognitive disability which I feel held back her physiological progress. I grew up with to say the least a disinterest in sport, it's only in recent years I've realised how important sport is to develop the mind and will to win. Your story is such a shining illustration of how important this is, beating all the prognoses by miles and miles! We're very active members of Headway the brain injury association – Headway Gwynedd branch and have also supported the Different Strokes charity. Best wishes to you and your husband Mark and family.
Anthony PS Mark has my full sympathy!

Frank Wheatley (UK)

Kate, you are doing brilliantly. Your book will help many people to be positive. Rick is reading your book to Chelle. It might take him a while but it boosts both of their moral. Keep the jokes coming and I thought you would be quite a conservative sort of person, ha ha ha
Cheers and best of luck.

Isabella (UK)

Hello, my husband Mike had a brain stem stroke in 2002 and has been left with LIS and we have 3 sons. I am a nurse so I was determined to get him home. We relocated from N.Yorks and and now live in Oxfordshire with Mike at home with us. I would very much like to help others who suffer this nightmare.

Sinead (Ireland)

I was amazed and delighted when I read your story in Woman&Home; your story is one of a miracle. I didn't think it was possible for anyone to recover to the degree that you have after suffering a Brain Stem Stroke with Locked-in Syndrome. My dad suffered a Brain Stem Stroke with Locked In Syndrome just over 14 years ago, 2 weeks before his 46th birthday. Daddy is still alive, but over the past two years his health has deteriorated. He lives at home with my mum (aged 55) who is his main carer, my sister and I.

Erin (Ireland)

I was thrilled when I heard your story on BBC Ulster this morning 23 May. I had a stroke 5 years ago at the age of 46 and I feel as passionate as you about the power of the mind to overcome the hurdles to get back to as near normal. It is important to set targets and achieve each one in order. Like you I had three children s and I had to make a difference if I wanted my life back. Thanks for speaking out.

Edward (UK)

Just finished reading the book by Kate. One hell of a lady and not one to sit back and let life go by. I had a stroke 8 years ago at 50 and thought I was dumped by the world as useless, but there is a tomorrow. Well done Kate.

Emma (UK)

Hiya Kate, I just wanted to say what an amazing woman you are. I'm so glad you were able to fight through everything and raise awareness of Locked-in syndrome. I lost my mum in December 2005 to Locked-in syndrome; my beautiful mum was only 45. It honestly was the scariest moment of my life; no one knew what Locked-in syndrome was. I was given a web address to look up but never any real answers or support. Your experience will help a lot of people who like myself were scared but never realised what Locked-in syndrome is. Wishing you all the best x Emma.

Jim (UK)

I am normally a very busy person similar to you in the past. I just switched on radio 2 and listened to your interview. I am a young 54 years old and quite hardened in terms of emotions. I wanted you to know that in 10 minutes I had tears running down my cheeks. What a wonderful story of human strength, determination, mind over matter. I will order your book immediately and would like to make a donation of £50 to your charity. Let me know how I make the remittance. All my warmth. Good on you Girl!
    Truly Inspirational, warm regards,
    Jim.

Sam (America)

Just heard your story on BBC radio via iPhone stream. You've inspired me. We're about the same age – married with children here in the US. I will promote your book to our local running club.

Rosie (UK)

I read about your amazing struggle through your book Running Free, I am in the army (and supposed to be a tough cookie) but found your story so emotional. Tonight I watched the ITV show 'Holding Out for A hero) and was amazed and thrilled to see how fantastic you look, you are an inspiration. I am serving in Germany at the moment but if there is any way I can promote the charity, I would be delighted to help. Keep up the good work and I hope you go from strength to strengthxxx

Sandra (UK)

I was watching Kate on This Morning last week and heard about the charity. My dad suffered a stroke last June at the age of 48. Previous to the stroke he was a perfectly healthy man and regularly exercised. Thankfully he has made a good recovery, however he still suffers mild memory loss and his mood can be very erratic - he is very impatient and argues more than he used to. At the time a cause for his stroke was not found and so doctors assumed it was due to stress. I am very disappointed with the follow up care that had been provided for my dad, and as a family we have received no support in dealing with what he has been through. I think this charity is a brilliant idea and I really hope people who have suffered strokes, as well as their families, benefit from it.

William Jan 2012

Kate...I hope I can address you by your first name, my name is Robert and my daughter Lucy who suffered a brainstem stroke 3 weeks ago. Lucy was riding her pushbike with the whole family (all with helmets on) and fell off the bike when she hit a stone on the track. As a result, she suffered a ruptured artery in the neck, which then led to clots to the major arteries to the brain and a massive brainstem stroke. She is in intensive care and is in a 'Locked-in' state.

As you would be aware from your own experience, the family and friends are all in shock but have all rallied around. Christmas was very difficult with our Lucy struggling for life but she now appears past the critical stage but what confronts her now is something that you are well aware of.

Naturally we have all been learning very rapidly. Most us have read a book by Dr Norman Doidge 'The Brain that Changes Itself' and of course most of the family has already read your book and some are finishing it. We have even started to read it to Lucy hoping that your experience and determination will inspire Lucy to achieve a similar outcome to yours. Although Lucy has been locked in for only three weeks, we have been able to communicate by her blinking from the first few days. She has now been able to turn her eyes laterally up and down and she can now, at will, turn her neck all the way to the left and about half way to the right. She is now able to smile and cry of course) and her facial features are very noticeable. There has also been a little movement in one leg. As such as we are heartened that her brain is starting the rewiring process and while slow to start, hopefully it will lead to a similar experience as yours.

Lucy is only 36 years old. She is fit and has led a very busy lifestyle working full-time (mostly from home) whilst looking after four children. Like you, she exercises and runs (although not as enthusiastically as you) I know you are probably inundated with emails and calls for help. However, when I read your book, I was truly inspired and thought what a wonderful story to tell to our Lucy to help inspire her to fight and to ensure she is returned to her wonderful family.

We would love to hear from you with any words of wisdom and also would ask if we could communicate with you now and then to seek your advice, views or just get an injection of enthusiasm as Lucy travels the very difficult road that you have done so recently.

Kind regards
William

Jan 30th 2012 Robert update on Lucy

Kate.
Lucy has been improving very well over the last week or two. Lucy came out of ICU last Tuesday and is currently in the Neuro ward. Total ICU time just less than 7 weeks. The trachy came out yesterday so she should be moved to the rehab ward within the next few days. Improvements are.1. Improved mobility of right hand and arm. Can now raise forearm and touch her mouth with her fingers and move wrist around and back and forth. Can wave goodbye.

2. Mouth is now about half open and there is plenty of tongue and lip movement.3. After the trachy came out Lucy was able to speak a few words. She told me over the phone yesterday morning within a half hour of removal 'love you' which I could clearly understand. 4.Now lifting right knee off the bed and more vertical movement in right leg. 5. Left side still slower but there is definite muscle movement in shoulder, a little in elbow and in leg. 6. Still drinking small amounts of water [watching carefully]. 7. Her spirits seem good but naturally she gets concerned that the left side is not happening much yet.

We are trying to keep her positive and assure her that one side was always going to strengthen ahead of the other. I Kate. Thanks for your very kind words. And thanks, too, for allowing us to be part of your journey for the past 8 months. It really has been an honour to have been part of it and to witness your strength and determination...You have a very strong character and won't take second best. In being like this, you have progressed so far – and will continue to progress.

My reply to Robert on 31st Jan 2012

Robert, this is FANTASTIC! Tell Lucy she is a star from me! Left side- nothing happened for me until end may 2010 (my stroke was 7/2/10) keep getting F.E.S on her left side, keep her willing and push the neurons to work to fire up-tempo muscles. Get her to use every ounce of strength to make just one flicker happen. Brilliant, and how nice she said love you! X

The photo Robert sent me on Saturday 4th February 2012 was quite simply amazing.

It was a real trip down Memory Lane for me as the image shows Lucy's hand-written scrawled message to her dad. It reminds me of the time I had to relearn the alphabet letter by letter and learn how to write again.

The message Lucy wrote for her dad quite simply read: *'Look at what Lucy was able to do today. Made me cry when I received it. Lucy is having blended chicken and veg for lunch and blended macaroni for dinner tomorrow.'* Robert
Just reading this message from Robert and seeing that photo and remembering that his daughter is just 36 years-old –three years younger than I was when I suffered my brainstem stroke is quite poignant. What great progress she is making! Keep fighting Lucy! I hope I can meet you and shake your hand one day or perhaps you can join me for a walk in the beautiful English Peak District. That is a promise I will definitely keep.
Another message from Robert 'Kate, It is Robert. We spoke last week about our daughter Lucy who is in locked in. Is there a chance you could have a chat with our Lucy on Skype sometime suitable to you? We can set it up in the ICU ward with a PC.'

Finally, I have to share my husband Mark's innermost Facebook thoughts with you. As I have said before, he does not find it easy to outwardly show his emotions but this post sums up his perspective of the last two years.

MY HUSBAND!
Mark Allatt, Sheffield, UK February 2012

Having been through two years of the most challenging times ever imaginable, from Feb 7th 2010 when I was told my wife, best friend and mother of my kids would not survive the night or best be a 'cabbage' for the rest of her life to the present day – when we see some normality coming back shows the range of experiences we have been through.

Our family and friends have worked tirelessly to support us, but what Kate has been through is the stuff of our worst nightmares. Seeing her motionless in hospital, limp, weak, unable to breathe, eat, control her bowels and in effect live just about destroyed me. It's bad for the victim; however, I can tell you my pain is forever. I'll never get those dark times out of my head.

Kate's strength to make only positives from negatives is unique to her. She never hid away and kept everyone strong with huge determination. The way she reached out to everybody via Facebook from hospital meant everyone knew what she was doing often before I did!

Her progress has been amazing. But bloody hell, she has worked for it. She will not rest until she gets where she wants to be. But she is very fragile. Her exterior hides complete turmoil – a consequence of her horrific experience. She goes into very dark places and she has finally accepted support in this area. We are all very worried that her desire to help others and raise awareness of this terrible condition is helping others but hurting Kate. She daily puts herself through torture to visit and support others, I see the fallout from this work and ask: 'Why do you do put yourself through it Kate?' Her response is: 'this is who I am now. I want to help others.'

At times, I just don't get it. But I am the proudest husband as a result of her generous spirit.

I know there are times Mark and the kids think I spend to much time on Facebook but they are also proud I am raising awareness about strokes – even though our spacious kitchen doubles up as my home office hub where I communicate to people from around the world.

I often visualize each and every one of my 'supportive friends' sitting down and enjoying a cuppa. (In photos they send, some of them in their 'former' pre-stroke life, they are either laughing or smiling.) Strokes can happen to anyone. People open up and share their worries and fears as well as their good times and breakthrough moments.

Facebook messages (and all emails, texts and letters) from stroke survivors are so exciting to receive. I sometimes wonder how isolating it must have been for all of those stroke patients born in a different era when there would be no shared information or knowledge at the touch of a button. Lonely and frustrating, I'm sure. They would have been cut off from the outside world with only their thoughts and immediate family for company. If I could have chosen to live in an era when I had my stroke, it would be this one.

According to Wikipedia, it is estimated that in 1993, the Internet carried only 1% of the information flowing through two-way telecommunications. By 2000 this figure had grown to 51%, and by 2007 more than 97% of all telecommunicated information was carried over the Internet.

In 'Wikinomics', Tapscott and Williams highlight the explosion of social networking.

The authors say: 'Mass collaboration is not only the most significant driver of success in today's marketplaces, it's helping to transform the way we conduct science, create culture, inform and educate ourselves, and govern our communities and nations. Networked models of collaboration and innovation can bring the prepared manager rich new possibilities to unlock human potential. But to succeed, one must challenge the conventional business wisdom that has companies and other institutions mired in twentieth-century thinking.'

My charity is all about helping others but it also gives me an opportunity to explore all the interesting stuff, views, and medical comments, survivors' stories, advice and feel-good responses from people in different time zones, recovery stages and personal situations. Just to see stroke survivors and their carers type a humorous line or two shows that you cannot keep laughter locked in!

I would like to add one last comment from Dr. Norman Doidge, author of 'The Brain That Changes Itself' for all my Facebook friends to think about. Let me know your thoughts on what he has to say.

'The competitive nature of plasticity affects us all. There is an endless war of nerves going on inside each of our brains, if we stop exercising our mental skills, we do not just forget them: the brain map space for those skills is turned over to those skills we practice instead.'

Thank you Facebook Friends!

Chapter 15 –
Analyze This...?

My first protégé, Pete from Perth, Facebooked me recently after I'd asked his permission to use his real name in this book. I had written in my usual, blunt, unique way.

'Pete, I'm such a dick! I totally forgot to ask your permission to use your words in my second book. Can you agree or not to me using?'

He replied:

'Well I have used you in mine so why not as long as its not of ill nature, I don't give a shit, good luck Kate xx'

So, I responded:

'Not ill nature but shows how we still have retained our humour through it all :).

Then Pete concluded our 'chat' by writing,

'Bloody funny times yes, but I think your heads messed up and it makes you hysterical. Hey! I was kicked off the ward a few times for laughing and waking others up when i had ridiculous laughs like you said, like a constipated donkey ha ha I can control it now and my laugh isn't so embarrassing thank God, xx'

It made me think of just how much I'd changed.

True, I found things even more funny now. Even when I don't want to laugh like I did SO loudly with Alison at our daughters' school leaving assembly which she found utterly mortifying. Or my embarrassing nervous laughter which had puzzled mourners turning to me and my wheelchair at Alison's beloved Dad's funeral. I even laugh hysterically when I am trying to reprimand our kids which must be totally confusing to them at the time. So much so, as I have already explained, I even had to develop the 'T' for timeout sign, so they would know my escalating laughter was actually me being mad not a comedy turn! Interestingly, Andy Davies laughed so loud during Christmas Day prayers 2011 in the hospital chapel I'm told his family were totally humiliated – though I know people get used to this post-stroke *Comedy of 'Inappropriate Laughter' Errors*.

For all of my inappropriate laughing, I do genuinely find stuff funnier than ever. I even have to blame my 'stroke laughter' for it, when I was genuinely having a hilarious moment. Do you remember me telling you how Alison annoyed the doctor after I'd fainted and she was thoroughly testing my reflexes? I soon knew I was ok and hadn't thought I'd had another stroke, but we started mischievously amusing ourselves at the kind doctors expense during another five hour spell in the Royal Hallamshire hospital. Alison sums me up when she says, 'You conveniently blame everything on your stroke now.' Well, only sometimes.

My stroke has heightened all my emotions and at times brings the worst out in my behaviour. I do accept that I am totally obsessive. I was driven before but now I can even drive myself mad! (Poor Mark!) If things aren't done within a short timescale I find myself very stressed and I often exacerbate people around me.

If I want a website building or leaflets designing, I know I seem ridiculously demanding to others who are often better equipped to prioritise their workload. In truth, I wasn't easily able to switch off before but I'm worse now I've had a stroke. If I ask someone to do something for me in return for payment, then I need and expect to be told an expected delivery timescale by them which they follow. If this timescale slips (and I look inept as a result) then I morph into some kind of overly stressed, deranged woman! I pride myself on being responsive to others and I only expect similar courtesy back. That's why I despise inefficiency. Truthfully, I should not aim so high.

I'm sure psychoanalysts would have a field day with me. Am I suffering from the emotional damage of being a paralysed mute for so long in hospital?

Did I spend too long out of control, with nothing but my thoughts in life that now take my new found control to a whole new level?

Am I just plain selfish, self-centred and abusing my severe brain injury with its repercussions to simply curry favour and make excuses for my behaviour?

Am I a parent/wife/ fish out of water adapting to three kids who have grown up beyond their years, during my 8 months of enforced absence? Do I just need to re-learn how to be a parent and wife again after focusing on just myself over the last two years?

I know I stress my kids and Mark with my impulsiveness. Sure, I don't always see the big picture like I didn't with my charity initially or how I would enter the swimming pool in Majorca, but I am a doer. I don't like to talk about doing something, I just want to get on and do it. But I accept I make mistakes in my haste.

I've learnt one huge lesson that a popular Mum doesn't necessarily make you a good mum. Almost all can bear kids, but not everyone knows how to handle them through the ages. Yes, I was trendy, popular, slim and successful – all those media stereotypes about capable juggling career women/mums, but I failed to give my kids consistency and enforce boundaries. I've realised that boundaries are easier to police if your kids have more respect for you, rather than being their buddy all the time. But I do also think some parents are unnecessarily stifling because they are too strict. There is a happy medium to strive for.

During my expected meltdown in November 2011, I relented and took some help. My life had been deliberately so frenetic that I had no time to look back to my harrowing early months of 2010. But when I stopped, boy did everything hit me like a freight train. So anti-depressants and Cognitive Behavioural Therapy (C.B.T) were organised that very next day, even though this would take three months to get underway. By the time I actually met the nice CBT lady at my local doctors surgery, she was somewhat surprised to say the least!

Why? I hadn't become a shadow of that person she had read in my first book since November 2011. On the contrary, I was alive, kicking, laughing and back to the Kate I was inside. There were photocopies in front of me which she was going to use for my first assessment. When

I explained how I'd almost finished writing my second book in the eight weeks since my referral appointment, her jaw dropped. She was gobsmacked. Finally, she got her words out and gave me a huge smile.

'Here was me thinking I'd get you writing down a few of your emotions on a page to screw up, then blow me you've gone and written a whole book!'

We chatted about me and my feelings for half an hour and the rest of the time was spent on my kids and Mark. She suggested we see a specialist child psychologist but also explored some strategies for my difficult youngest child.

I was told I should not ban Woody from seeing his friend Nic, the only constant in his life over the two years, because that was actually emotionally cruel to do. Instead I should ground him from seeing any friends. I'd not thought of this. Sure Nic was his Achilles Heel, but I was making his fragile, emotional state worse. I immediately started rewarding his good behaviour with *Moshi Monsters* toys rather than punishing bad behaviour, where the punishments often escalated.

I knew that breaking the news of 'special family help' wasn't going to be well-received by my kids. They had endured, (because they really hated it) weeks of educational psychologists at school during my absence. I guess people were only doing what educational guidelines specified in giving therapy to school age kids who were about to lose their mum. They hated the person they were assigned to seeing and totally refused to accept that I was going anywhere, let alone die forever. Rather than helping their emotional state, these weekly sessions would remind them what they were missing. Kids are resilient and found ways to cope but each time they bounced back, they would be bought back to earth with a thump, as they were made to discuss their mum, my story and their memory boxes. (They thought if they didn't make a memory box, then somehow mummy would not die. A kid's logic!)

It's true to say that India was in her last year of primary school and still harbours some anger at the way my illness interfered with her SATS examination preparations. She is so keen to do well and achieve like her friends were. She is far more diligent than I ever was, which means she will be motivated to succeed.

So we had our first, family psychology session. My kids sat through and contributed for two hours and were fantastic. Initially, they wanted me there, but in future I would do the ironing if it meant I didn't have to hear their thoughts. (I didn't do ironing before my stroke and detest doing it now, so that gives you some idea of how hard it was to hear their candid views about me.) Our clothes had never been so pressed and neat (a stark contrast to our crumpled lives) as I took on this domestic goddess role with vigour. Mark was shocked to see his shirts ironed to perfection and joked there were some plusses after all as I had seemingly turned into one of the *The Stepford Wives*.' Not that I never kept things at home shipshape, you understand!

Surprisingly, Woody loved the 'nice lady' and Harvey was more open than I thought. Better still, they were happy to see her again, so result! The following week India refused to see the psychologist, which was a surprise as she had enjoyed her first session. I think it was more about her control, my surprising reaction and her teenage hormones!

I told her she could miss the following week's session but she decided to go. I told her why it was a good idea for her to open up with a professional.

Two reasons – a) I think she needs it. b) I need her to have it because I don't know how to parent a teenager, so I need help and guidance on what to do!

I still struggle with my sexiness and feelings of being worthwhile. I still always feel that, unlike the *L'Oreal* advert, 'I wasn't worth it!'

I also have the legacy of the worst Post Traumatic Stress Disorder. I often think my life is some sort of surreal dream and that I'm actually on a bed in Osborne 4 waiting to get my nappy changed by a nurse. That PSTD is getting better but it's still there. I have no emotional defences now.

I strived so hard to be return back to my house with my beloved children and Mark, that I take normal family disputes hard, very hard indeed.

I'll give you an example. I have a row with a family member. I feel it's a 12 out of 10 argument on the scale of 1 to 10. Consequently, I'm left feeling a desperate, emotional wreck and often in tears and awake all night long.

Whoever I was rowing with sleeps soundly because they consider it a 'normal' family dispute.

I am more than prepared to deal with my behaviour changes with cognitive behaviour strategies but I'm totally unhappy to unlock the box of emotions I felt during my eight months in hospital and the 18 months back home. What purpose would that serve to bring up all those shite, deliberately buried memories?

I now know why my grand 'Papa' never opened up about his time as a Desert Rat in north Africa in World War Two. He didn't want to unearth those very dark and distressing memories as by doing so, I truly believe, you relive painful memories. I am aware such memories can creep into your everyday life if you are not careful. There are times I have been in Sainsbury's and had to pinch myself to make sure I am still not on hospital dreaming about shopping. I think that anyone who goes through trauma, they only reveal the 'tip of the iceberg.' The really deep and buried stuff is not allowed to surface and I totally 'get' that. I suppose that is why the whole concept of therapy can be seen as both a good thing and a bad thing. I do know I don't want to delve too deeply. Although analysing distressing events is par for the course when undertaking therapy, I do believe in moving forward. The future should not always involve dredging up the past. But it is from the past we often learn the real truth about ourselves, our innermost fears and anxieties. And I know that there are thousands, if not millions people, walking around each day with their very own 'baggage.' But when and where does it get dumped, if ever? A conundrum to say the least!

Do I totally like myself?

No. Not yet and only at times when I use my dreadful experience to inspire and empower others. I can't see why Mark would love me, after all I'm such high maintenance and don't make for an easy life. Though it is certainly not boring!

Was I stunned and shocked at P.C David Rathband's untimely suicide this week? (March 2012) Yes, I was totally floored. He survived being shot in the face by Raoul Moat, campaigned for his remarkable Blue Lamp Foundation charity and had to suddenly adapt to life as a blind person. He must have been so emotionally alone and tortured. I understand how he felt great helping others. Yes, it's a distraction from the nightmare's and all the shite, but he lived in a lonely, dark world. I identified with his public persona and his private torments. I feel for his friends and family again now. It leaves me wondering if it's always the best thing to survive a disaster. I think it depends on individual circumstances and just how a new life pans out for someone – and the support they do or don't receive. I have been very fortunate but I am well aware that 'happy endings' are few and far between.

A HUSBAND'S PERSPECTIVE – Mark's thoughts on the last two years.

'You only really know how much something means to you when it is all taken away. On the 7th February 2010 at 6.09pm, I will never forget the time as I was looking at on the DVD player when our world changed forever. My best friend, wife and mum of our lovely kids looked me in the eyes, said something I had never heard before and slipped off the sofa into a heap. She was clearly in a bad way.

I also lost my ability to think. Panic took over and I just said,

'Are you OK?' No she was not alright, even I knew that and I am a bloke !

I watched in shock as the whole next 24 hours passed me by. Then came the message. Kate's situation was desperate. Survival was not guaranteed and if she did pull through, then she would require 24 hour care. I wept. Then I wept some more. Then I asked why? Nobody gave me an answer.

Kate has beaten the odds. She has proved the medical profession wrong and made a recovery that is only dreamed of in fairy tales. Why? There is only one reason and that is... she is Kate. I'll explain more. She is, as my mum always said, 'never going to be easy.' I laugh out loud as I hear those words. Kate's charm, beauty and personality means she is a great woman with the ability to be different. She has an 'I can do that' attitude and loves to prove people wrong. She builds great relationships, provides help and support, takes the piss, challenges the norm and always has a scheme up her sleeve, I could go on and on.

Kate is my life. Without her I am nothing and back then I was nothing without her. However, I had to learn to survive, not just for me but for our children. I was hurting but they were devastated and they gave me everything from support to being a pain in the arse. I had prepared myself for only what occurred on that day. I did not look forward and I did not look back. I just took everything in front of me and thought, 'OK Mark, just deal with it.'

That was easier said than done. I went into a shell. I had lost my soulmate and I did not know what to do or say. My emotions went sterile. I had none. I could not show any and nothing in life gave me any pleasure. The kids needed me and most importantly I needed them. Kate needed us all but how did we make this happen?

I am an engineer, now turned commercial person. But I reverted back to engineering. I am, in reality, a person who always thinks in black or white, yes or no, zero or one. I became that logical person 100%. I had to work things out. I had no strategy as nobody gave me a list of things I needed to know or do. I had no end point. The doom merchant gave me one which I did not accept. I soon saw Kate fight for another outcome which medics said was impossible, I could only try and manipulate what I saw was possible for the best outcome for our family. There would be tears. There would be hate, there would be disagreement, but I felt that I had the opportunity to do my 'bit' by even though I had no idea what to do or how to do it.

So the impossible began. Here I got help. Family, friends, people in the village and my work colleagues seemed to somehow be able to keep me sane, focused, wind me into action and, most importantly, ensure I did not fall apart. I thank them all. When I needed them, I never asked, they just knew. When I was low, they picked me up. When I was daft, they were stupid with me. They read me like a book and gave me what I wanted at the time. They were the true heroes and became a cornerstone of providing what I did not know I actually needed. Instinctively, they carried me along with their friendship and stopped me from sinking.

I have stories of ridiculous comments, such as my mate Richard Williams' unintentional offer that went way beyond the realms of friendship and became a long-standing joke about what friends do for each other in time of need. (the wedding speech 'gag'). James gave me a warm blokey hug like I will never forget. Alison, just being there, not judging me on my coping skills but making sure I was OK. Chris for his mastery of friendship, Jaqui because she was so clear in her mind when I was confused and Anita because she was so giving. I could go on, so I will. My parents did beyond what they needed to. Jo because she did stuff and didn't bother to look for anything in return, Dave because he knew I hurt and he just gave me a hug, Jan because she made me fight. In reality, everybody did a bit, all different, none more then the other as they all just did what they could. That's what friends are for.

Kate challenged herself and everybody who nursed her. But now we have a new challenge, she is back home and we have to get on with our lives. Surviving a brain stem stroke is one thing. Surviving the aftermath is another. Life suddenly got difficult. Our family had been ripped apart and now we had to put it back together. Easier said than done. I had gone into a shell, I did not want to be hurt anymore and our kids had suffered during her mum's absence. India had taken on total responsibility for the family. She was mature beyond her years, but going through a change of schools, facing challenges of teenage friends and just growing up she started to suffer. I could not help as I tried and failed. She needed Kate so much but she was stuck in a hospital bed and could not help her. She soldiered on, without a whimper, but she was building up issues which would erupt later.

Harvey went quiet. He always goes in on himself. He needed a mum to help his tender and caring side and he needed a dad to keep him strong. Both were missing and he went quiet. I knew he needed support but I did not give him what he needed.

Woody was young and in a way unaware of the complexity surrounding our family. He did not know what he needed, but he needed something I did not and could not give and, as a result, he started to fall apart.

So all three of us were were in turmoil, but we were still here. That's what is was like each day. When Kate was back home, I got up and helped her, saw to the kids' needs, went to work, came home, helped Kate and the kids and crashed into bed. I was on autopilot. I did all the right things but I did not give back what they actually needed. Here I was, Mr Engineer, yet I couldn't fix things. I did everything correctly but without showing any emotion. I had none. It had been knocked out of me. For me, every day was about survival and not about showing love. I had to get through this somehow. I said my family needed me and I needed them, but in reality I missed the point. We needed love. I had none to give. That's the legacy of a stroke as it hits the partners and children too. We never realised at the time just how we had been affected. I cannot emphasise this enough. But we have got through somehow.

There is no guidebook. Well, I say that – but Kate has provided more information to help families than I had access in the early days of her stroke. For me it is all about what I have learnt on our surreal journey from 7th Feb 2010 until now. Here is my summary recap:

Think and think fast.

Ask questions, but look for facts don't be emotional. But, yes later on DO show your feelings.

Be positive, not for yourself but for the patient, they need to believe in you.

Don't be frightened to ask for help, everybody want to help, but often don't feel bold enough to ask if you need it, so just make it easy and ask people for help.

Kate is the patient but kids are victims. Don't forget them as they need more than you think.

Kids are very reliant. This is a positive and negative, just be aware of it.

Humour, you need loads of it. With Kate I needed more than most.

Family are brilliant, but are also grieving and hurting.

Everybody needs normality. Its not easy but keep things as close to normal as possible.

Go to the pub, if all the above don't work, then just get pissed!

So with those words of wisdom, none of which I really took on board, we come to the final stretch of the race.

It never over, but it does get easier, hopefully ! Kate has been amazing, but I have come accustomed to the monthly 'mum's dead' and don't worry Mark, she's Ok but...' calls. We have had some amazing experiences despite the massive challenges. Let me share a few.

Our first night away at a hotel in Rotherham, Kate wants a bath, she gets in but can't get out. Decision, do we call the duty manager for a lift out of the bath? Fortunately, I got her out myself.

I bought her a new red Mini Cooper. We went for a spin and quickly discovered that here left leg could not operate clutch control. A whole hour later, having driven three metres, I got out and walked off in a huff.

The bloody Zimmer frame! She banged into everything with such a commotion in the middle of the night just to wake me up when she wanted a wee.

Her manic laughing, when she is supposed to be serious. It almost got us thrown out in the middle of the kids' Xmas school assembly.

She crashed the mini going though a six-metre-wide 'fast' moving gate. I give in!

The standing ovation she got at the media awards. Everybody cried except Kate. She just laughed. Typical!

So more than two years on, we are all making good progress. It's hard to rebuild a family given the issues we have had to deal with, but we are getting there. We all need inspiration and that's the key, Kate provides it. It's that simple. Believe! I am going to say it here in this book (yes, Mr. Engineer is now going all emotional...in print! The words are here in your book Kate, for posterity). I LOVE YOU India, Harvey, Woody and YOU Kate!

What went on inside our children's heads?

In hindsight, Mark and I wish we could have been there more to protect our kids at the time.

My children lost their mum and life as they knew it, so were understandably angry and emotionally alone. 'Anger is a normal emotion,' according to my child psychologist.

Chapter 16 –
When A Friend Is In Need –
Alison's words of wisdom

'The 7th February 2010, the day of Kate's stroke, is a date imprinted on my mind forever. As a friend (I am proud Kate acknowledges me as her 'best friend') of someone who suffers from such a life changing 'event' how are we to act? How involved are we allowed to be?

After all there aren't any rules of engagement. There was no book telling us how to cope. I didn't want to impose on Kate's family, but standing on the periphery waiting for news is not my strong point. I acted on impulse on the second day I arrived at Kate's house.

Mark, Kate's mum Jan and mum-in-law Ann were there to greet me. They opened the doors and their hearts as they welcomed my offer of friendship and support. From then on, a deep bond grew between us. We all loved Kate but needed each other for support. We cried together and we laughed together. Our emotions were all over the place as we tried to make sense of what had happened to Kate and her new life in hospital out of our world. Just being together in the early stages was essential. Thank you for that everyone.

Jan, Ann and I didn't know each other very well. They had heard stories of Kate and my escapades, but early on realised the value of our close friendship. I was thankful to feel included as they discussed Kate and what she needed. I was desperate to see Kate too. I had to let her see that I was there for her.

The first time I saw her in hospital, it was upsetting. She was in a large blue chair in what I could only describe as a straightjacket. It seemed to hold her arms to her body. She looked so wrong. So different from the Kate we loved and knew. Kate had always been so active and healthy and this seemed so unreal.

Kate's reaction at seeing us was total shock. There were heart-rending sobs but no sound, as only her eyes moved. Tears rolled down her face. I could see her anguish and felt powerless to help her.

Anita and I just went into nurturing mode as friends do. We asked Kate if we could wipe her tears and nose to let her keep the bit of dignity she had. Of course, she could not reply at that stage but we wanted to treat her with respect. We left the hospital and broke down, but we never cried in front of Kate. We had to stay strong for her sake.

We visited together for the first few weeks, as it was easier to bounce off each and kept the atmosphere light. I always remember the very first visit when I arrived in the hospital car park and turned the engine off. I felt physically sick and nearly turned back home to my comfort zone. This is one of the cruellest things I've ever seen. Someone so incapacitated – Kate so young and in her prime trapped in a living nightmare.

I gave myself a strong talking to as this was Kate in there, my partner-in-crime and a friend like no other. She needed me and I could not let her down in her time of need. As soon as we walked in I saw the relief in her eyes. We became her voice.

As friends we couldn't make decisions but we could ask nurses for the day-to-day care, the human contact. The nurses were doing a fantastic job keeping her alive but we were bringing her back to being Kate. It is vital for stroke survivors to have choices and the right to communicate.

In hindsight we should have pushed for Kate to do the communication board quicker.

We should have found out about the leg cramps and the inability to sleep. The list of 'should have's' goes on.

The visits were something Kate needed as it was 'friends' time and we could help her temporarily escape from the nightmare she was living. Newspapers and books were great to pass the time away. My flower arranging amused Kate no end. My job, as I saw it, was to make Kate smile. We re-visited old times again and again. I could get my own back on Kate; the bonus was she couldn't answer me back!

Her eyes swore quite a lot as she blinked out profanities. Many times I refused to spell out a whole word, which I knew was overly negative. Sorry Kate. I now know, how frustrating that must have been.

There are a lot of low times in which I would let her feelings show. The thoughts she communicated were confused, deep and dark. Listening was crucial. It was painstakingly slow with the word chart but essential for her to exercise her 'voice'.

I couldn't leave Kate if she was crying. My rules were that she could cry for half my visit and then stop being mardy. I did not want her to feel too down and at times I was firm with her, which I feel she respected.

This was our own version of therapy.

The more Kate improved, she made me realise how focused she was. This was her job and obsession. She was going to walk out of hospital if it killed her. She did break rules (I did help her with a few!) She pushed boundaries. But then Kate always did so none of us were surprised with her full-on attitude to break free.

Kate welcomed encouragement from friends and, when anyone visited, she urged them to do the exercises without her therapists. Not the other way round.

These exercises were so small but moved her onto extremes, so note regular exercises are a MUST. At times they seemed so futile, what was the point if there was no immediate improvement but then suddenly there would be a movement.

I remember one episode in Osborne 4 when we were permitted to freshen up Kate's mouth with apple juice. This was done using a pink sponge on a stick. All I had to do was wipe Kate's mouth inside a few times to give her the pleasure of a taste she knew so well. The problem was Kate enjoyed this so much; she would often clamp her teeth on the sponge and not let go. This was only supposed to be three dips of the sponge, but they had the wrong person, as I was on Kate's side. I couldn't deprive her of that one luxury ...one pot of apple juice later! Though she had to be on lookout for the nurses, as we would have been in big trouble.

One visit Kate was very low. Her psychiatrist took me to one side and said in a matter-of-fact manner,

'Kate has to come to terms with the way she is, her expectations are too high, whereas our expectations are down here (she pointed at the floor) she needs to lower them dramatically.

I totally didn't agree and told her,

'NO, you need to raise your expectations.'

You see, I knew Kate, they didn't. I knew what she was capable of.

I do understand that medics are looking out for patient welfare, but hope and persistence gets people a long way.

We all have our fears. Mine are WASPS!

One visit I was sitting talking to Kate and a wasp came – I ran.

At the nurses bay I stopped and thought, 'Oh No! Kate!'

So I ran back to the end of Kate's bed and tried to wheel her out despite the fact she was attached to tubes and wires. I saw the wasp again and had no such qualms about saving myself as I ran to the nurses to tell them about the unwanted insect which I feared would sting Kate. Luckily Kate thought this was hilarious. I put myself into her place – the fear of not being able to move is too much for me – particularly. I need counselling just thinking about it.

The first of everything we did was a lot of fun. Like Kate's first ride in my blue VW beetle car with Anita and Ann in the back, whilst we were doing our version of Thelma and Louise, just keep the foot on the gas! (A prison break.) Kate returned to hospital in high spirits.

It felt so normal whatever 'normal' is. Eight months in hospital makes you forget. How Kate went back into hospital after her taste of freedom I'll never know.

Kate's speech was very difficult to understand when she started to speak. We didn't care. What mattered was that she was speaking again. Besides, we were able to get used to her new way of speaking and sometimes even make fun of it. Kate did not want to be treated with pity and we knew it. Mark would tease Kate mercilessly, as he is a real wind up merchant. Kate took it in her stride and never complained, laughing at herself most of the time anyway.

I understood a lot of what Kate said early on. I now joke with her that it was because I knew what she sounded like drunk having had many merry nights with her and these evenings of revelry now put me in good stead as her interpreter.

Many of us are guilty about turning a blind eye or walking if we feel out of our comfort zone. Persevere and use your humour to lighten the situation. Kate liked the sound of her own voice anyway and has not stopped talking since. Making up for lost time. (Every now and again, I look back and remember the peace!).

Only joking, its fab you are back chatting away and catching up for lost time.

Kate needed a lot of support emotionally and physically. Mark got the brunt of it. You can do and say horrible things to the people you love. With friends you behave a bit better, but they won't let you get away with being mardy anyway. Kate struggled with personal confidence in many ways. She wasn't worthy. She would often question why Mark or her extended family wants her as she was? Why would friends want to be friends with her? She viewed herself as a 'cripple' and wouldn't look at herself in a mirror. (Nor would I with all that grey hair Kate!)

When you read an autobiographical book, you instinctively make a judgement on the narrator. You ask yourself whether you like the person. In this instance, you are reading each page and asking yourself if you like Kate or not, if she is right or wrong in what she has to say and if you like her as a person. Is she right or wrong? Selfish or unselfish? Haven't we all been those things at different times of our lives? In my eyes, this is a book which shows the real Kate. It is a very honest book. Yes, at times – and I say this as a friend to Kate whom I love and respect greatly – she has been all these things. Right, wrong, selfish and giving. Yet, when you are in survivor mode you have to be selfish to survive and life's rules go out the window. My experience of Kate is one of total admiration and I am so happy to have my friend back from the brink of death. We could all have so easily lost her. She is a one-off and I am so proud to be her friend and see her recover from Locked-in Syndrome – and get her roots done!

Kate's heart is in the right place and she means well. She has lots of insecurities from what life has thrown at her. Life in her world is anything but boring. She will have ups and downs and what she has had to go through I am not surprised. But those close to her love her enough will make sure there are more ups than downs. She is an inspiration.

I have my own support. My husband, my kids, my mum and dad, Lesley, Lisa, Anita and Jaqui. Something we will all never forget. Hopefully others will learn from Kate's story and we are all proud she chose to laugh at herself as well as share the bleakest moments. Life is always exciting when Kate is around.

Alison, March 2012

Chapter 17 –
Gonna Fly Now!

So what has changed since the start of writing my second book?

Now I totally realise that not everyone can 'fight' his or her illness. I do not want those who are Locked-in or who have not progressed as well as me to somehow feel they are not trying or fighting hard enough. I often try and imagine I'm a stroke patient reading about Kate's Great Escape. It would, I imagine, feel like being superglued to the starting block in a prostrate position with your mouth gagged and your body trapped in a restrictive Houdini style outfit while the 'stroke champion' was approaching the finishing line to loud applause.

I'd be SO annoyed if I thought people expected me to make more of an effort to unshackle myself, raise myself up and show more effort. 'For goodness sake, can't they just wiggle their right thumb first just like Kate did, get up and get a move on?' It would be easy to feel like a complete failure if others thought you were not 'fighting'. I understand that my 'success' could completely infuriate others who have not been so fortunate. As I have repeatedly said, every stroke is different and it is not a race! Don't give up because your progress is taking a slower or different path to mine.

Nobody has ever said expressed envy or jealousy or said that my achievements have really made them feel worthless. I do believe that my story is inspiring for others who find they are going through a similar experience to mine.

Young father Mark Ellis, just 25, is one of many Locked-in stroke survivors who have contacted me. He gives readers an insight into how it feels to try and get back to normal. More importantly, how he reacted to reading about my 'speedy' recovery.

'It did seem quite unfair at first, but when I realised all the work I could put in I knew deep inside me that if Kate could do it then it is possible and it has been. I am breaking free after Locked-in syndrome after 14 long agonising months but I made it. I would just say to anyone to never give up on their recovery.

'I have no jealous or hard feelings towards Kate and she has made a miraculous recovery and I only compare myself as I want to be the same as Kate. I would only say well done to her and watching her gives me more strength and determination. Before I met Kate I was less motivated after over a year of speech therapy and occupational therapy. After I met her, I knew I needed to keep fighting more if I wanted to get back to what I class as normal as I was so used to going places in my wheelchair and if I wanted to speak I would have to type everything out on a 'speak it' phone application. My speech is slowly coming back but I still use a wheelchair for NOW until I get stronger.

'Since meeting Kate and her husband Mark they have both helped me on the recovery front and Mark has helped my wife Amy out by saying, yes, this is normal for NOW but things will change for the better. I have a 15-month-old daughter who has been incredible and just accepts me for who I am. She was only two-weeks-old when this happened. I've missed out on so much but I won't miss a day of her life any my goal is to take her to school on her very first day and I don't care how we do it, I will manage it if it kills me.'

Linda Wheatley, mother of 29-year-old Locked-in mum-of-two Michelle, was happy to write some words specifically for this book.

'We feel Kate's breakthrough has given us all of us a positive outlook. The only envy we have is that Michelle did not receive immediate rehabilitation and we would not know what the outcome would have been. Because of Kate, the whole family has been totally positive to Michelle's recovery and we are constantly complimented by people around us because of our positive outlook.'

Both Mark and Linda's comments, and those of hundreds of people from around the world who have been writing to me on Facebook, and Twitter – not forgetting all the text messages which ping into my iPhone daily – prove to me that my story gives them hope. I know some people get their illness diagnosis late and therefore don't have time to take on a fight against it. However, I feel very strongly that if you want something bad enough, you will get it. More importantly the carers, friends and close relatives have to stay positive too.

I have used the word 'normal' a lot in this book. I know that 'normal' for me is not about being good or healthy and it is about not being 'average.' Who wants to be average?

I do accept my new 'normal', even though I proudly announce that 'I'm disabled' when I need to queue jump, or if I'm too lazy to walk to a public loo, as opposed to the immediate shop loo. Normal to me is not being average but also, being able to pick my kids up from school like all the other mums. Being able to do their homework or riding a space hopper and STILL embarrassing them on school Sports Day. Telling my children off. Hugging them. Feeling sexy for my wonderful husband Mark and actually wanting and enjoying, as Bill Clinton would say, 'physical relations' as a normal loving wife again. Becoming integrated with my old wider circle of friends and not being scared of being among larger groups of friends or strangers. In fact, the attitude of strangers who know nothing about what I have endured, has been quite enlightening!

I always loved delivering cheap one-liners and after my stroke I enjoy them even more!

One example? I was in Macclesfield for a school reunion when the pub landlord moved us into a rear room for a lock-in. (quite apt!). As I shuffled in my new stiff boots, quite quickly, I thought – he asked me a question, which immediately wound me up.

'What's up with you love? Lost your callipers?'

My friends looked on, not quite believing what their jovial barman had said. I was horrified inside but stayed calm. How would he cope with my answer?

'I'm really sorry but I have had a stroke,' I replied in a gentle voice, hiding the fact I was upset.

The man's face was a picture and he was SO apologetic. He offered me free drinks for the rest of the evening and said, 'that's the best put down I've ever had in 45 years!'

It also reminds me of that time in a supermarket when I asked the checkout lady to open a plastic bag, because I couldn't get into it, she slowly said...

'THIS IS HOOOW YOU DOO IT.' in a singsong voice as if she was talking to a three-year-old or as if she thought I was a very 'slow' adult in need of her somewhat patronising demonstration in front of a queue of other shoppers.

I was horrified, angry and embarrassed by her rudeness. In a very controlled way, I stared into her eyes, as I wanted to see her reaction to the words I was going to say in front of her.

'I'm really sorry, I've had a stroke.'

I could sense her body momentarily freeze. Her face went white and she proceeded to quickly undo all my new bags! Funny how appearing 'helpless' always brings out both the worst and best in people!

I'd gone from a 70 miles a week fell runner to a totally dependent baby to frail pensioner and then to an unsteady toddler in just 8 months! © Kate Allatt

In terms of stroke recovery, I've gone through a plethora of emotions from the positive 'prove 'em wrong' attitude in hospital, to anger, denial and finally acceptance. I do think I will continue improving and progressing but I'm happy for that to be more organic and less forced. It's true I've gone from a baby (nappy-wearing, dribbling and not speaking), to toddler (learning to walk, speak write and use the loo again), to pensioner (wheelchair, crutches and in need of home-help), and then back to an independent 40-year-old woman. It could have been worse. It could have happened in just one day! That would have *really* messed with my mind!

I recall my holiday to Cornwall in May this year. I must have been quite deluded to think I could put on a full-length wetsuit, go rock-pool fishing, bob around in the sea without nearly drowning and attempt to walk around the headlands like I always used to. The sort of holiday activities many mums would take for granted. It came as a huge shock when I quickly realised I wasn't almost back to normal and a long way off from the old Kate. I found myself being an observer rather than a participator of my family's fun as I sat all day on a chair huddled behind a windbreak!

Now, I'm happy to drive 'Rocky,' my red mini convertible (NOT an automatic) enjoy fell walking in the spectacular Peak District and chase around after my kids. I have a great legacy with my books and Fighting Strokes charity and am excited about my new role educating, informing and entertaining groups of people as a motivational and inspirational speaker. My ability to continue to provide support and guidance to other stroke patients and their carers in the UK and around the world makes me feel I am giving something back to life. I am immensely proud of all of my professional achievements, which culminated in my recent meeting with the Rt. Hon Nick Clegg MP.

The coalition government came to power following the UK General Election on Thursday 6th May 2010 – three months after my February 7th stroke. At the time, I was not aware of the political shake-up let alone that my local MP was now Deputy Prime Minister! My hospital TV viewing was Jeremy Kyle, not Jeremy Paxman. Heated debates about divorce and DNA tests. Not devolution and devaluation. Such escapism filled my dull and depressing days during my early days in hospital. Some may say the show's real life rowdiness could be compared to the 'audience uproar' in the House of Commons! I had not been cognitively impaired but perhaps my daily helpings of reality TV shows had left me further removed from the world outside and I was disconnected from other people's everyday concerns.

I was determined to get up-to-speed quickly to learn about and government health policies and the more I learned, the more I realised many stroke patients seemingly get a raw deal. In some respects, I was one of the lucky ones. I had a lot of questions I wanted to ask Mr. Clegg. The only common ground we shared was that we both have three kids. His public persona had always seemed affable enough but would he listen to what I had to say?

Alison accompanied me to his rather tatty Sheffield Hallam constituency office with one of Mr Clegg's four stony-faced protection officers. We arrived early and he delayed our appointment as he was expecting a call from No 10. We wondered if David Cameron was the reason for our waiting game. Alison couldn't just sit still and she could not resist trying to get a smile from the man who resembled an extra from the film 'The Bodyguard' – there I go again showing my age with all these film references! He was the silent type. We guessed he was probably not paid to make light-hearted-small talk.

The silence seemed to last forever. Alison, being the sort of person who likes to break the ice, suddenly asked an inappropriate and cheeky question as she glanced in his direction.

'Don't you ever get bored following Nick around all day?'

The man's stern face broke into a wry, though unprofessional smile. There was something about Alison I was dead jealous of, which was how she *always* got away with stuff in the way I definitely could not!

Suddenly, Mr Clegg's personal assistant informed us that we only had 15 minutes with him, so I knew I had to make this meeting matter. Furthermore, my long-suffering trustees had previously and politely told me to keep a lid on my motor mouth!

Suddenly we were ushered in and we sat down before our new Deputy PM. I had some pre-set questions. But I was not going to go in firing on all cylinders. I had to choose the right moment! I introduced myself and was pleasantly surprised that my MP had been well briefed, as he knew all about me. As I handed him my Fighting Strokes poster, wristband and first book, he put them aside to ask me all about my stroke, the effect on my kids and what my experiences must have been like as I lay Locked-in and fully compos mentos in ICU. He seemed sympathetic as we chatted for two minutes, before I abruptly announced that I wasn't there to talk about my story as I had some questions to ask for my charity and supporters. He looked a bit taken aback.

I was very business-like! I managed to speak assertively and clearly. My speech was not yet back to 'normal' but I got my points across and my questioning would have made Jeremy Paxman proud!

I reeled off my questions. There were quite a few!

'Do you know that strokes are the third biggest killer behind cancer and heart disease, but it is set to become the second biggest killer?

'Do you also know strokes affects kids, and I know of at least one very young child, not yet at school, who is Locked-in?

'Are you also aware that only five per cent of the national stroke budget is spent on post hospital rehabilitation?

'Why is there a postcode lottery in stroke care? If I had lived in another area, I may not be here, now, having this conversation.'

'Are you aware that I wasn't given an MRI scan before my stroke, even though I had the classic stroke symptoms?'

At this point I took a breather and handed Mr. Clegg a Daily Telegraph article, which listed them. He looked as if he was going to speak, but I had not finished yet!

'Why is the National Health Service cutting so many costs? Surely this cost cutting will end up costing the economy, welfare and NHS even more in the long term?'

The Deputy PM looked thoughtful as if he had understood the points I had raised.

'So, finally, why am I here?' I was on a Paxman roll, really getting into my stride now as my motor mouth was fully revved up. My voice had not let me down once and I forced my final words out as I looked at how many minutes had ticked by on my watch. I did not want 'stony-face' officer to be summoned to show me the way out just yet. I had my most important question to ask.

'I would like you to get me an appointment with the NHS Chief Executive, Sir David Nicholson MBE, so I can discuss stroke rehabilitation, please.'

Mr Clegg gave a short pause, and then spoke in front of his note-taking PA.

'No, I'll do better than that, if you can travel to London, I'll get you a meeting with the Minister for Health.'

I was just about to argue my point, as I clearly hadn't absorbed what he'd just said.

'But...'

Alison kicked me in the shin to shut me up. The magnitude of what he said dawned on me, so I held back my inappropriate thoughts of 'B****y brilliant!' and politely replied with a big smile.

'Thank you very much!'

Later, I went on to ask various questions that the health minister would be far better placed to answer. We then had a photo taken of us with Mr Clegg and left. Just 14 minutes later, it was handshakes all round and a case of a job well done and another experience for the journal. He was indeed a 'reet' (as Yorkshire folk say) honourable man in my book!

Incidentally, Alison had been there in her role of charity trustee and secretary but actually only managed to write three words in the whole meeting!

I realised that if you passionately believe in making a point then you should do it. It was quite liberating to know that the Deputy PM had taken me seriously. Believe me, when you have lost your voice for a very long time just knowing that you are being heard by people who can hopefully affect the decision making process feels tremendous.

My new life is all about finding a balance between fighting my corner and fighting for my cause and simply enjoying life – the one I could so easily have been denied.

I have still yet to find a replacement for fell running that enabled me to enjoy peace and quiet and exercise in the fresh air because I now have with my hip, cardio and balance.

As a bit of a bed lover before, I am delighted to announce that I can finally enjoy lazing in bed again. I have not been able to lie – in or sleep regularly through the night, but I can now, as my body clock seems to have reset itself. Perhaps my disruptive sleep was a reaction against a life spent in bed all day, through no choice of my own. Or it could have been a reminder of the fragility of life, the relative shortness of it and my new desire to exploit every day and leave this world knowing that I have achieved something and left a legacy. The plus side was that all my great ideas happened at 4am when I would excitedly write them down!

I have analysed and over-analysed personality, my situations and ME. I've learnt a lot about my emotional baggage and myself. I have issues that go back years! There are parts of my personality I don't like, so I keep working on to improve them. Everyone is a 'work in progress' whether they have had a stroke or not but its legacy has probably made me over analytical of life in general. I am often asked if I analyse why I had the stroke in the first place and NO, I don't go over this in my mind. There is no point. I'd rather look forward with optimism and hope, not backwards with bitterness.

I realise I can make things happen and I am a self-starter. I am a survivor for sure, I always have been whether it be fortuitously avoiding a certain fate in Lockerbie in 1988 or pretending that my au-pair job in America was all rosy when it wasn't. Or surviving alone in Australia without a bean in 1995.

I am probably more comfortable with the new me now. I see and understand my weaknesses and am trying to listen more.

Mark and I have also had a breakthrough too. He recognises his strengths and weaknesses and is trying not to erupt in anger or frustration, (which I'm sure is a lesson Woody learns) and finally recognises that he put up an invisible and impenetrable force field, which meant he didn't show or receive affection from me or our kids or his family especially over the last two years.

He refers to the months following my stroke as 'my living death'. He emotionally detached himself because he thought I wasn't going to survive and then when I didn't he couldn't stop himself from his emotional detachment. He sees that now with our kids and me and it was never anything personal, just his way of coping with the awful situation. He would arrive from work in his suit and sit at the bottom of my bed rocking to and fro. Nobody ever expects events like this to happen to them, do they?

Mark was trying to hold it together and look calm. He must have been so shell-shocked and I definitely understand that now. Inside my mind I just wanted to scream,' Come and get in with me and hold me tight.' Of course, he never knew I needed him to do that as I was wired up to machines and looked so fragile. He was scared of all that had happened to me. How could this pale, inactive woman with all the tubes and monitors possibly be his fit and healthy wife?

There is deference to doctors and a certain way of behaving in hospital as you feel you have to 'play by the rules' and now I understand that everyone behaves in their own way. But the lack of tactile hugs was a major issue for me, particularly as I could not initially communicate to Mark that I needed him up close and personal by my side. I was terrified and feared I was dying. Scared I would be allowed to die. When you feel you are battling to survive, you just want another human to comfort you, as you feel so vulnerable and alone. I cannot stress enough how lovely it feels to share hugs with Mark again.

I am genuinely pleased to say that the air between us has been finally cleared, the romance and humour is back and we are genuinely, as Alison declares, 'coming together' as a couple. The result of our enforced separation, animosity over key events, our family issues and having to re-build our married life, has been a huge challenge but we are back on track now and our renewed wedding vows and sheer thankfulness we are still together and coping with whatever life throws at us makes us realise the true meaning of those words 'in sickness and in health.' I do hasten to add that it will never be all smelling of roses!

We still disagree on certain issues but no one can take away what we have been through or our resilience as a couple. We have a greater understanding of each other and have gained a better understanding of the crazy journey we have been on. The fact it happened 'out of the blue' and turned our lives upside down has made us appreciate that nobody knows what life has in store for them and we are determined to live life to the full and to encourage our children to grow up with the knowledge that life can be full of unexpected events. They all know that despite the upheaval they have had to deal with, they are all greatly loved and we are proud of them.

India is much more settled and happy. We have shared both our perspectives. Our future is bright and she is turning into a lovely, caring, affectionate and attractive young lady who oozes confidence if not too many hormones!

Harvey, my loving complex middle child, has returned to his more balanced sensitive yet cheeky ways and is always a lot of fun to be around. He is mischievous like his mum. The events of the two years will also have affected us all but I'm sure we will all have learnt to turn those dreadful negatives into positive experiences.

Woody is emerging with much more self-control and less anger as he gets much more of my attention. He loves his 'huggles' and seems to be responding to my new boundaries and rules. I'm sure, he, like the others, will always challenge me as a mum. But then again, I guess that goes with the territory!

I have to talk about Alison here. You see, Alison, being a professional hairdresser is very easy to talk to. If she wasn't always a natural born listener, then her job certainly ensured she would become one. Like me, she has a few of her own long-standing close friends, but she is without absolutely any doubt my personal best friend. Alison is a very loyal friend to all her friends. You could say, (in the nicest possible way) 'if she sees you as a special friend, then she'll be your 'dog for life!' She gives my life a solid foundation. She is calming, reasoned but massive fun to be around. You could say her massive support, coupled with my instant paralysis, finally helped me kick my rather embarrassing adult-thumb-sucking habit. (Did I just admit to that?) Her balanced views and judgement give me a warmth and understanding of life and all of its foibles like I have never known before

She is SO perceptive. She is so special to me and I thank my lucky stars every day that we chatted over a hot drink on the first wintry day when we met with out children and she bizarrely and rather un-coolly announced her membership of the Caravan Club (an in-joke!)

Alison has taught me to talk a lot. Actually I always did that before! But, seriously, she has encouraged me to face the world again and speak to others as my voice has returned. The single most important thing Alison did for me was showing me how to laugh again. Those charades back in ICU or attempting to dye my grey roots so I would feel more attractive when I was transferred to Osborne 4 or insisting I spent full whack on my 40th birthday watch from Mark's parents or making my step dad wear, nothing but a lime green mankini, in a Sheffield park from a beach in Cornwall!

We always had great fun together and turned any event into banter and laughs whether it was sledging (while we forced our kids to go to school in the snow when they could have had the day with us) or racing down her high street on hair stylists cutting stools late one evening. Then of course there were the late nights after a few glasses of Cava or blagging trips on expensive yachts. We have a catalogue of humorous moments, which have brightened up our lives and many wonderful shared memories.

Alison is naturally more socially aware than me, which is why I unknowingly seem to offend or annoy people with some of my comments. I want to get a cheap laugh and in doing so I naively go too close to the bone at times. She has also gently taught me how to be a less stressful, selfish mum or wife. She encouraged me when I was down and helped me get through the tough times.

She intuitively knows when I'm upset, depressed or saddened and is always quick to comically fix the situation. I know I won the Extraordinary Woman of the Year 2011 award but in my book she is so deserving of this accolade as she represents a blueprint of what a true and loyal friend should be in my opinion.

My extended family struggled to provide much physical or emotional support when I left hospital during this year; I believe they were all frazzled emotionally and physically exhausted. Perhaps their noses were pushed out of joint with my contractual media stuff? Perhaps they were just so relieved I was actually back home, even in the dreadfully disabled state that I was in? I do acknowledge that they were convinced I'd likely die, and if I didn't, I would require 24 hour nursing care. With a stroke brain injury, the patient appears outwardly normal but in reality, I was far from it. However, I do hope this book at least draws a line under my last two years, they understand me more and we can begin to re-build and move forward in 2012.

The whole parental discipline thing can be tricky. I was worried my mum's laid-back approach could unwittingly undo all the good work I was doing to get my kids in order and under control.

Without doubt, I needed the break. But I couldn't risk her laid back approach undoing my newfound parenting control.

You see she was always able to offer short bursts of Nana fun and excitement, which often meant she broke the rules. She had a quirky edginess that my kids loved. For example, she would always buy them sweets when she visited, irrespective of how bloody awful their behaviour had been for me. It's interesting how her being a Nana, is so different to how she was as a Mum for me. I guess I can look forward to handing back hyped grandchildren, as I return home, in a few years!

I am very fortunate to have my top mates Jaq and Anita. The friends I feel most 'me' with. Their loyalty is second only to Alison's.

Their unwavering support for me was tested once again, as I had an emotional meltdown in November 2011. Fortunately, that sense of desperation, low self-esteem, confidence and sheer hopelessness hasn't continued into 2012! I feel buoyant and optimistic about this year ahead and everyone has noticed I am the focused and efficient Kate again and am far more confident. I would tell all stroke survivors to believe they will finally getting their life back on track and don't give up!

Self-belief is so important to recovery even though there will be many times it feels as it has taken a battering. My decision-making skills and general outlook on life have been enhanced and I don't hide myself away anymore. My energy levels are increasing all the time and I have a new zest for life. But it DOES take time and you have to be aware of your limitations.

I understand that becoming happier has been a gradual process. As has the way I view challenges. I would say that it is necessary for the way you perceive your ability to do something. If, according to Carol Dweck's *Mindset: The New Psychology of Success'* you have a 'fixed mindset' you will think your abilities are set in stone. Your life will be all about proving yourself, and if you fail, you'll think you are no good and will shy away from challenges. On the other hand, if you have a 'growth mindset' you will believe your talent will grow so failure is feedback to tell you you're doing something right. You are pushing yourself to the limit in order to improve.

I discovered this recently on an extremely cold day on January 23rd this year when I liaised with photographer Richard Hanson for my Blacka Moor photo shoot. Much of the time I wore my warm favourite cosy jacket with my hood up. I had my new Adidas tracksuit on and the shot was 'all about my returned fitness, strength and confidence' and the fact I loved being back in the Great Outdoors where I truly feel alive and happy. (I hated being trapped indoors in hospital SO much!)

Just as I took off my protective jacket, the heavens suddenly opened and icy sleet fell down. Although I am all for the 'natural look' and for many years had become used to being out in all weathers. I was beginning to feel like a drowned rat. Like any woman having her photograph taken, I wanted to look my best! Just my luck for this to happen when we'd checked weather forecasts and desperately wanted things to pan out well for the shoot. Suddenly, behind Richard, the most magnificent full rainbow appeared. It's colourful striped bands of brilliant light arching across the windswept moorland against the backdrop of a dull, grey sky.

Although I have seen countless rainbows before, I felt real joy at seeing this one. I knew I wanted it in the shot. I climbed down from the bench and Richard directed me where to stand so he could capture me in front of it. This unexpected 'high' on a dismal day made me realise life is *still* full of little surprises. Richard, buzzing with enthusiasm and creativity, then asked me to climb a small hill as he fired off a few more shots of me 'in my favourite habitat.' Back at home, my teeth were chattering and I felt as if I had been out with adventurer Bear Gryllis but do you know what? I felt so energised and happy.

It is quite poignant that even a proper outdoors photo shoot had been a truly liberating experience, a challenge even. Richard allowed me to take a peek at some of the images on the LCD screen. There I was looking strong, confident and free – totally 'me'. It was like looking at the old Kate again. As they say, the camera never lies.

I like the new me!

Mike from Mi-To Therapy has been a real superhero in my body's complete metamorphosis and the way I see myself. He has most definitely changed my life beyond what anyone could have ever believed possible.

Mike helped me exceed my initial and totally unrealistic recovery goals in both record time and at a record level.

Now, in the way he supported me and my seemingly unrealistic goals, I am inspiring other survivors like Andy Davies from Birmingham and Mark Ellis from Chesterfield. This is what *really* makes me happy at the moment, apart from being with my fab close family and friends.

From a psychological perspective, Mike was a fantastic sounding board for my deepest worries and anxieties in the way I seem to be for other families and is largely responsible for 'Where I am at now' – both physically and emotionally, at the beginning of 2012.

He was a physiotherapist, personal trainer and psychologist in one! He deserves a medal for what he's done for family, my friends, and me but mainly for giving me my life back! He proved once and for all that medical plateaus do not exist, though post hospital stroke NHS rehabilitation funding does! You just have to have the self-belief and work bloody hard and team to help you!

I'm definitely operating at a much higher level now, with my increased empathy and desire to give back to others, which I find hugely liberating. But the flip side is that I am more socially withdrawn, especially in larger gatherings of friends where I'd have once thrived. I do need constant reassurance now, even though I can be accused of being unintentionally blunt. Nobody intimidates me now, and I feel a bit like an old person who has earned the right to say and do exactly as they please.

I may continue to inspire and empower people both here and all over the world but I have also learnt so much about me, my immediate and wider family, friends and as a mum and wife.

I often sit and question why I have been SO driven since my stroke?

Of course I was heartbroken at the 'loss' of my kids for nearly eight months. No Mum can ever love anyone more than their own children. But I was in denial about the loss of my former life and former love – running. I also think my own childhood feelings of insecurity; loneliness and lack of tactile affection came into play. Don't get me wrong, I was always loved but people found it difficult to show it. There were low aspirations of me in my own family, as I was the only girl until my sister came along 14 years later. I was also a middle child (don't get me started on this!) and all these issues have contributed to my obsessive personality and need to constantly prove people wrong.

Coming home was lovely at first, as I was deeply institutionalised. Yet home quickly became a nightmare from which I often wished I could escape. It was if the family Sat Nav that guided us through the ups and downs of everyday life had vanished into thin air. We had all lost our direction and were going round in circles or trapped on Blacka Moor in a fog without a compass. We knew all that was familiar to us and we were 'nearly there' – but just couldn't seem to find our way out. As we all leaned on each other, it felt as if we were all emotionally wounded in our own different ways from the impact the stroke had on our family.

Actress Sharon Stone, who had a stroke in 2001, has produced a YouTube video with herself as the stroke personified. She says...

There's something you should know about me. I'm cold. I'm calculating. I get what I want. If you get in my way, I'll wreak havoc upon you. I can leave you weak, limp, twisted, confused. If you want to live to see tomorrow you answer to me. And you answer quickly. I am a stroke.'

I would say that her words, in the great James Wood-directed video for the American Stroke Association, could apply to the family of the stroke survivor just as much as the man or woman who has been affected. Yet nobody realises this until much later. Only now, with the passage of time, can my family look back at the whirlwind that developed and even begin to understand it. I was at the eye of the growing storm and we were all being buffeted around with nothing to cling onto. When you are actually in the centre of the upheaval you are oblivious to what is happening to your family. Then slowly, as you realise things are out of kilter, you feel quite helpless to 'fix' things. How can you when you yourself are not yet fully fixed?

I strongly believe that we all should have focused, personal goals to try to constantly improve our own lives, whether that is personally, professionally or of course in terms of our individual health. However, we must always believe in where we want to go in life and work hard.

When I think about my total and sustained Locked-in state, I have already achieved far, far more than anyone (medic or otherwise) ever thought I ever would. The fictional character *Forest Gump* summed this up for me now though.

'*I do just want to stop running now!*'

I have remarkably run on the first anniversary of my stroke; run/walked/run 1.5 kilometres three months before my second stroke anniversary; won Extraordinary Woman of the Year 2011 with one hell of a three night break in Majorca!

It's fair to say that it's been a pretty incredible last two years! I have learnt first-hand that you need,

Self-belief, strong goals, tons of support, knowledge and inspiration.

Having a child-like sense of humour has really helped, as has Alison, my partner-in-crime and distracted me from looking backwards too often.

What's more I have grown from the experience in more ways than I ever thought possible. You could almost say that I operate at a higher level than I did before from my stroke. It has been documented that many people who have overcome major life changing events operate more efficiently. There is an element of realising we have limited time on this planet and every day counts. I guess that is why I wrote Part Two of my life story so quickly. I feel I have so much to say about being a stroke survivor, right now at this moment in my life.

Will I take on further running challenges? possibly not, but if anyone has a future, non-vertically challenged expedition or fundraiser they would want me to take part in, then I'm all ears.

However, other than that, I will happily drift in the background and give myself (and you!) a bit of a break.

Writing this has book been easy as my thoughts pour out. It has been great therapy!

I need to focus on continuing to rebuild all of our family members lives. I'm a changed person as are they. I have to continue adapting to the new and improved Kate Allatt and my role as wife and mother.

'It's not the circumstance, it's your reaction to it that counts.' The view of Dr. Al Siebert in 'The Survivor Personality'.

In the words of well-known fighter and national hero, Sir Winston Churchill.

'Kites rise highest against the wind, not with it.'

I have adopted this one of his as a personal mantra.

'Success is not final. Failure is not fatal. It's the courage to continue that counts.'

In my case, continuing on meant retaining my sense of humour. I could not let the 'enemy' steal that away from me and that is why I bizarrely imagined I was Rocky Balboa. I had to bring a character I admired into my mind that would spur me on to recovery. Trust me, when my legs got hairier by the minute (before my friends arrived with a Ladyshave and played a major role in restoring my sense of femininity) I often wondered if I was turning into 'Rocky.' I also feared my voice would end up lower than before. Thankfully, my special visualisation techniques had no ill-lasting effects.

I joke about my voice (It now sounds, more or less, just like before) as there are a few documented cases of those who have suffered strokes or brain injuries who awake from a coma to find they have and can only speak in a different language or dialect previously unknown to them – 'irregular repetitive speech syndrome'. To date, I do not greet people with 'How you doin?' in an American drawl. But if I am ever lucky enough to meet the man who played my favourite all-time film character, I may not be able to stop myself!

I will still remain wholly voluntary for my Fighting Strokes charity as well as embark on my own 'paid job', my speaking career (www.KateAllatt.com) as either a medical or inspirational speaker. After all, I have to make a living now and I feel I have the skills to do so. There is no reason why I cannot take up the reins of my business life but I will certainly aim for that much talked about life balance. I enjoy travelling, meeting people and of course talking! Perhaps I should have a link to my Curriculum Vitae here – updated to add the words, 'has the ability to laugh at herself'.

'When I started writing this book I quickly realised that I CAN unleash the lighter moments of my 'miraculous' journey, but in doing so I have an important serious message about early stroke rehabilitation and recovery. I really do feel I am holding a key to

'*Unlocking The Keys of Stroke Recovery*'.

This is one of my keynote medical speeches (physiotherapists, nurses, speech and language professionals and neurologists, etc). I also deliver my comeback inspirational speech. I certainly don't have ALL the answers, but I know I have definitely acquired a good understanding of the myriad of issues that relate to surviving a brainstem stroke with Locked-in syndrome, and I am learning more all the time!

For larger corporates I deliver more of an inspirational keynote speech I refer to as 'Life is limitless.. so aim high!'. I believe you can achieve anything you want to if you really want it.

Different corporate groups and charities, including the Sheffield branch of Wellbeing of Women, Royal College of Nursing and the Swindon Literary Festival, have already approached me in relation to my inspirational and patient talks. It would be great, in this year of the 2012 Olympics, goals and achievements, if others can gain a deeper understanding of what specifically brainstem stroke patients need and want, but also inspire people to aim high in life. I want to keep making an impact on improving people's rehabilitation, recovery and what they achieve out of life. To take my baton and pass it to others. Share information. Make a real difference and if this defines Kate Allatt, then so be it, because I'm passionate about this.

If this book was written in a totally factual and serious way without the fun flashbacks, I wonder if my message would be less powerful. I certainly think so. The human brain is remarkable, as is the human spirit. I HAD to keep a sense of humour. I do know I have a lot to give to others by telling my own personal stroke story. After all it is a story about ALL stroke survivors...people whose voices should be heard. Not forgetting their laughter too.

Today Sheffield. Tomorrow? Who Knows?

Lights, Camera, Action!

You know where to find me Mr. Stallone.

GONNA FLY NOW!

Kate Allatt 2012 'Life Is Limitless. You Just Have To Believe It!'

Two years in the life of Kate Allatt
January 2010-2012

 Severe migraine started mid January

 Attended walk-in-centre at 10.00am on Sunday

 Attended A & E at 12.00 midday on Sunday

 Suffered brainstem stroke at home 6.09pm Sunday. Suffered total locked-in syndrome

 Left ICU for Osbourne 4

 1st review

 Tracheotomy out

 First family holiday to Cornwall without me

 First spoke

 First assisted walk in 'baby stroller'

 Second trip to Cornwall without me

 Stomach PEG out

 Left hospital

 First anniversary run

 Jeremy Vine

 'Running Free' published

 Winner Extraordinary Woman Award

 My first disastrous trip to Cornwall

 Disney

 Summer holidays

 My second trip to Cornwall

 Holding Out for a Hero TV

 Girls on tour, Mallorca

 Percy Pud race

 Discovered Neuroplasticity and Prof. Doidge MD, Oliver Sacks and Ian H Robertson

Finished writing Gonna Fly Now!

Acknowledgements

I am proud this is a self-published book as I can break the rules a bit! However, I must thank my first publishers Accent Press and Alison Stokes who helped me write *'Running Free: Breaking Out From Locked-in Syndrome.'* Bizarrely, I relished the challenge of writing again and hopefully you will agree that *'Gonna Fly Now!'* is a natural, complementary partner to my first book but can also be enjoyed without reading the first gritty account of my true-life story.

I have included a few crossover references in my sequel as I feel it is important for readers to gain an insight into what happened to me on Feb 7th 2010 when I suffered a major brainstem stroke. I often can't believe it myself!

Writing my first book felt quite cathartic and my initial anger definitely spurred me on as I channelled its raw force to fight back to recovery and open up about my life-changing experience.

At the time, it was a 'shoot-from-the-hip' read 'both sad and funny'. *'Running Free'* gave me an opportunity to create a legacy or personal words, as does this book.

My precious children will perhaps understand why and how family life changed following my stroke. Others coping with illness may read my story and be inspired not to give up hope.

Both books may be useful as a 'practical and emotional' reference guide for other desperate stroke patients and Locked-in survivor families.

Over time, my anger has lessened and I have been able to unleash more of the lighter moments of my life, as I look back with a different perspective – hence this second book.

After all, laughter and humour are known to be great coping mechanisms and it would be so easy to become bitter and wear a 'why did it happen to me?' badge of belligerence. It is important that I retain my sense of humour and try to stay positive.

I have recently wondered if I should launch a 'Locked-in Laughter Unleashed' stand up comedy show as well as focus on my inspirational speaking. My stroke certainly provides me with a lot of material.

Truthfully, I find it harder than ever to filter and communicate my thoughts in a politically correct way. I understand this 'bluntness' is a common brain injury trait, which, on the positive side, does allow me to express stuff you all privately think, but daren't say!

'Gonna Fly Now!' is, by its very nature, a more reflective, considered book. Although I hope it is humorous when exposing my survivor personality 'traits', it also publicly lays bare my weaknesses too. When I finished writing this book, it became obvious that all my public and professional successes were being paralleled by my depressing personal failures throughout the year I left hospital.

I think it is important to 'tell it exactly as it is' so others who are going through similar experiences know they are not alone. Having any kind of stroke, Locked-in or not, impacts on you and your family in an unimaginable way.

I was the main focus as I was the one who was 'ill', yet my close family and friends had no point of reference on how to deal with the 'major event' and they just had to take one day at a time.

Subsequently, I felt it was important to publish the identities of those who have given permission to be included. But, at the time of writing this book, I have protected the identities of those people whose permission I was not able to confirm. Thank you everyone.

When I came out of hospital and was initially in a wheelchair I felt like shouting, 'Look at me, I'm ALIVE, and I'm not Locked-in!' Many people, who had not seen me since my stroke, saw a dribbling, pale, frail woman in a wheelchair and could hardly recognise me and my 'new look.' How do I know? They have since told me.

Locals, even those who had heard about my stroke through the 'dynamic village grapevine', were shocked to see me back in the community. I looked like a very different person to the one they had often seen jogging by prior to my sudden 'disappearance' from everyday Dore life.

One woman fled into a local Co-op to have a 'secret cry out the back behind the loo rolls' to find another school mum doing exactly the same! After they had composed themselves, they came out smiling and bent down to hug me and kiss my pallid cheeks. As I slowly asked 'How are you?' I heard my words sound feeble and strange. I SO wanted to be 'normal' again.

To many, I was seen as 'poor disabled Kate', not 'She's out of hospital and doing so well Kate.' To those people, who have told me how they perceived me at various stages of my recovery, I thank you for your honesty. I am not offended.

After all, the woman I saw in the mirror was not Kate Allatt but an imposter and I avoided my reflection for a long time. I gradually got used to my new persona as I focused on improving my health.

Others, apart from close friends and family who had regularly visited me in hospital, had to get used to the 'new Kate' and I understand this now.

These views give the reader an insight into the real disparity between a stroke survivor's perception of recovery, and the view from their able-bodied friends as well as strangers – many treat you as if you are invisible or just plain stupid.

Such perceptions may benefit others, whether it is at the patient's review stage or later on when the stroke survivor returns home.

All I have written so far are personal acknowledgements I have made about my OWN particular stroke experience and the rather surreal journey I have been on.

I had to include them here, as I am proud to acknowledge my own self-analysis, which has been poured into this book – with a healthy dash of Rocky's no-nonsense view of life.

I have come a long way on this journey and have had more time than most to analyse the 'real' Kate Allatt.

It once mattered, in my pre-stroke-life, if people liked me. Now, I know that such insecurities waste time and detract from my role as a friend, mother, wife and charity campaigner.

So what if people don't understand me the way I am. At least I am not pretending to be something I am not. I am like Marmite– you either love me or hate me. I don't need to be popular anymore. I cannot please all of the people all of the time. But I can jolly well try and please and accept myself – only then perhaps can I put this life changing event behind me and move forward. I can either nourish people or i can leave them with a sense of bitterness. Yes, call me the Marmite Girl. I can live with that! All that matters is that I am true to myself and true to those who support me. Don't judge someone unless you've walked in their shoes. I have been to hell and back but I don't want pity, I don't want you to necessarily like me but I do want you to know that there are so many people who have suffered strokes who need to be listened to. not written off. If I upset a few people trying to highlight their needs, then so be it.

Now, I want to acknowledge some of the many people who have played such a vital role in my life and my recovery and getting this book and its message of hope to all of you.

To my wonderful husband Mark, undoubtedly my unsung hero. Thanks for giving me the opportunity to recover in the first place, for coping with my entire range of mood swings and for embracing my next hair-brained idea! Understandably, a lot of readers and Facebook friends have had great sympathy for you living with me. Oh what you have to put up with!

Truthfully, I am more able to recognise what you have done for me over the last two years – not what you haven't done for me. I know I am lucky to have you Mr. Allatt. I am proud to be your wife and honestly, there are times when even I wouldn't want to be married to me! Thank you Mark, for being a valuable and committed trustee for my Fighting Strokes charity as well as an excellent husband and father to our three children.

Thank you India, my caring eldest child. Stay happy, hugging and talking – though not quite so much as me! Your ability to become such a great 'stand-in mum' when I needed to lean on you is not only forever appreciated but makes me very proud. Your resilience and ability to stay strong will benefit you in the future, I'm certain.

Thank you Harvey, my sporty, cheeky chappy middle child. You have had to adapt and embrace a new level of patience and understanding around me. Keep letting your wonderful sensitivity shine through and I promise not to give you a dead-leg!

Dear Woody, my youngest who always says it as it is. Thanks for being so naïve. You innocently forced me to push boundaries in hospital when you helped me to speak my first words again and helped me become – a near normal mummy – again.

I hope that we can all put this massive trauma behind us and be happier and more settled in life.

Caring top mate Alison, thank you for your daft humour, listening skills, loyalty, patience, alternative parenting tips and selflessness. You have taught me more than you can ever imagine over the last two years and I would include you as a member of my family.

Thank you my friend Cheryl. You must be in no doubt how instrumental you have been in making this book happen. Your advice, friendship, ideas and editing. You have been the voice of reason when I worried whether I had been far too honest or not nearly candid enough. Your 'if in doubt, leave it out' advice has been totally invaluable on every level (and you've stayed chilled about my brackets and exclamation marks!) Not to mention a few 'choice' words. I recall your initial input during our lazy lunch at our local Cricket Inn last September when the Rocky concept developed when I revealed I was 'writing another book – but with a lot more fun'. You who ran with the idea – even suggested holding Rocky film nights and charging friends a small fee in aid of Fighting Strokes. Who knows if this idea will catch on in Sheffield (globally?)...but Cheryl, can I NOW have my Rocky II DVD back please!

Special thanks to excellent Sheffield-based photographer Richard Hanson (hansonphoto.co.uk) who got covered in mud at Blacka Moor when taking my back cover photo, which perfectly encaptures the real 'up-for-a-laugh Kate', and my newfound sense of freedom. Your creative, fun ideas (I really do look like I am going to take off into the air) helped me forget about the abysmal weather. I must add, for the record, my feeble and funny jump attempt was NOT photoshopped!

Thanks to Allan, at Allan Morris Design Associates, who has worked tirelessly to design my charity and book literature. You have interpreted my front cover brief so cleverly.

I wanted to symbolize my sense of feeling as free as a bird after my hospital incarceration when I could only blink to communicate. The font was chosen to show 'immature' writing, as I had to re-learn how to form letters on the page and write properly again. Your design is spot on!

Big thanks to my printers at Riasca; especially my old friend and rugby 'widow' Stewart. Not forgetting Jeremy who is making sure that my book reaches the right places. Thank you! To my charity patron Rony Robinson and cartoonist Richard Smith (www.richsmithillustration.com), thank you.

To my fellow stroke survivor and campaigner, Sue Sandars, a 'big bloody thank you' for your support and friendship.

Thanks to my supportive new American friends, Kate Adamson, Ernie Kasper Bob Miller and west coast resident Rich Marsh, who have all supported me in my often lonely and totally misunderstood world. I do hope I can meet each of you one day.

Thank you finance whizz Pete Chambers. I really appreciate all your amazing help last year with Fighting Strokes and your patience is appreciated.

To my Woodford 'travel counsellor' Donna Waddington, my best friend from schooldays. Thanks for your continued friendship and support.

What additional superlatives could I possibly add about Mike Lee at Mi-To Therapy? You are an extraordinary physiotherapist and remarkable professional and believed in my passion to run again. I cannot thank you enough! To my other fabulous trustees – Chris and Rob and non-trustee advisor, Lec, thank you! To all at my local Virgin Active (Ex-Esporta) who welcomed me into the gym with open arms and played a key role in my recovery plans, not forgetting all the gym-goers who showed genuine interest in my goals and got to know I was a real person and not the 'disabled woman'.

To Jaq, you are a brilliant friend and mentor who has kept my feet firmly on the ground during your challenging year as chairwoman for Fighting Strokes. I will always remember your words of encouragement, including...

'You can't eat an elephant in one go!'

Thank you Anita, for being a hugely supportive, loyal friend. Thanks for your wonderful singing and, along with a great many other things, introducing me to Tuesday walks on Blacka Moor, which I look forward to every week.

Thanks to all my best friends' husbands – James, Chris and Bill for showing true friendship and support to Mark and our family and being there for us whenever we needed you...and thanks to all the other dads, mums and step-parents.

Thanks to Dr. Colin Feltham – Emeritus Professor of Counselling at Sheffield Hallam University who, after reading my first book, offered his professional expert view on my personality! He said that I 'pretty well' fitted the profile of Al Siebert's *The Survivor Personality* and also pointed me in the direction of Norman Doidge's *The Brain That Changes Itself*, and the *Handbook of Adult Resilience*, (Reich, Zautra and Hall).

Dr. Feltham went on record saying that 'none of these has Kate's gritty authenticity.' Also, that I reminded him of Uma Thurman's *Beatrix Kiddo* character from Tarantino's two *Kill Bill* films. A comment also suggested by a Facebook friend! Perhaps I should warn Bill! (The only one I know is Anita's husband). Anyway, thanks for your personality analysis and I will aim for some extra bedtime reading... or should I take up martial arts?

Finally, thanks to all of you who have contacted me. Many of you have suffered a stroke, are Locked-in and are at various stages of recovery. Or you may be carer, relative, medic, or physio. Many of you are writing on behalf of a friend or relative who is a stroke survivor. All your stories are valid. No two strokes are the same. All of your words mean so much to me.

I recently came across two quotes from the actress Audrey Hepburn.

'True friends are families which you can select.'

And *'Nothing is impossible, the word itself says "'I'm possible!"'*

I was fortunate that my close family and 'family of friends' believed my recovery were possible. New friendships are developing all the time and the resounding message is of hope and positivity. You are inspiring people. Thank you for sharing your stories.

To all of you, wherever you live in the world, continue to believe in true long-lasting friendships and the 'possible'!

Kate Allatt 2012

Richard Smith ILLUSTRATION

Web: www.richsmithillustration.com
Facebook: Richard Smith Illustration
Mobile: 07723 710 756

Delighted to support the wonderful work of Fighting Strokes

True forgiveness takes time. Fact.

Memories can never be erased.

Building self esteem, confidence and self worth is a slow process and ongoing.

Kate Allatt (April 2012)